Basic Anatomy and Physiology

BY H. G. Q. ROWETT M.A., F.R.S.A., M.I.BIOL.

THE RAT AS A SMALL MAMMAL

DISSECTION GUIDES
I THE FROG
II THE DOGFISH
III THE RAT
IV THE RABBIT
V INVERTEBRATES

GUIDE TO DISSECTION
(Dissection Guides I–V in one volume)

HISTOLOGY AND EMBRYOLOGY

BASIC ANATOMY AND PHYSIOLOGY

H. G. Q. ROWETT M.A., F.R.S.A., M.I.BIOL.

JOHN MURRAY
ALBEMARLE STREET LONDON

In this new edition, apart from minor amendments at numerous points in the text, the opportunity has been taken to re-cast the section on homeostasis and the function of the endocrine glands in the light of new thinking on these topics

First published 1959
Reprinted 1962 (revised)
1966 (revised), 1968
Second edition 1973
Reprinted (revised) 1975
Reprinted 1977, 1979

Printed in Great Britain by Jarrold & Sons Ltd, Norwich

0 7195 3200 0

Introduction

THE HUMAN body is made up of an enormous number of tiny units of living material called **cells**. These cells are of different kinds and are grouped together to form **tissues**. The tissues are used to construct **organs** concerned with special functions. For convenience the organs may be considered to be grouped into **systems** but the functioning of each system is closely related to that of the others. The body works as a whole with each individual cell requiring food and oxygen and having to get rid of waste materials. Each cell is sensitive to any change in its surroundings, though in varying degree, and misfunctioning of one part of the body may upset the whole.

The study of the cells and tissues is called **histology**. Because the special features of the different kinds of cells are closely bound up with the structure and functions of the organs in which they are found, there is no separate chapter on histology in this book.

The study of the form and arrangement of organs is called **anatomy**, and their method of functioning, **physiology**. The anatomy and physiology of the various parts of the body is dealt with system by system, with cross references to indicate the integration of the whole.

Diagrams are used as far as possible with the minimum of written description.

General Plan

The body consists of axial parts—the head, neck and trunk—and two pairs of limbs.

THE SKELETAL SYSTEM

The skeleton is composed of two types of tissue, **cartilage** and **bone**.

CARTILAGE is softer than bone, less rigid and slightly elastic. It forms the temporary skeleton of the developing fœtus, but is gradually replaced almost entirely by bone. Cartilage is retained throughout life on the articular surfaces of most of the bones, and as the nasal, laryngeal, tracheal, bronchial and costal cartilages—see pages 10, 19 and 87.

BONE is a rigid, non-elastic tissue hardened by much calcium phosphate. There are two types of bone. **Hard bone** forms the surface layer of all bones and the whole of the tubular shafts of long bones. **Spongy** or **cancellate bone** is found inside the hard bone. The spaces in spongy bone are usually filled with red bone marrow. The large **marrow cavity** in the shafts of the long bones is filled with yellow bone marrow.

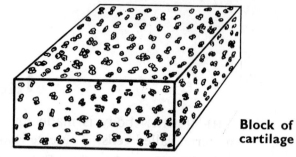

Block of cartilage

OSSIFICATION is the process by which bone is formed. Most bones replace cartilages though a few are formed directly in membranes.

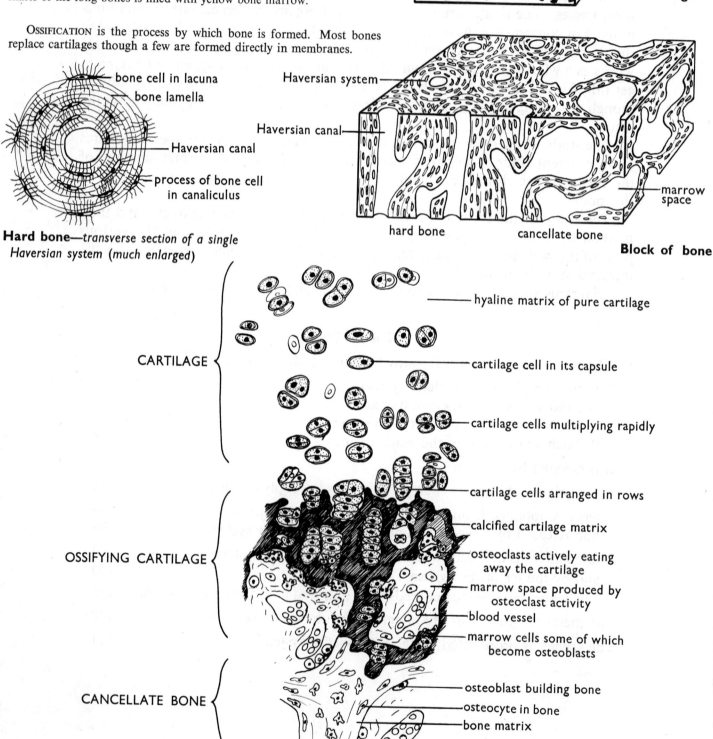

bone cell in lacuna
bone lamella
Haversian canal
process of bone cell in canaliculus

Hard bone—*transverse section of a single Haversian system (much enlarged)*

Haversian system
Haversian canal
marrow space
hard bone
cancellate bone
Block of bone

CARTILAGE

hyaline matrix of pure cartilage
cartilage cell in its capsule
cartilage cells multiplying rapidly
cartilage cells arranged in rows
calcified cartilage matrix

OSSIFYING CARTILAGE

osteoclasts actively eating away the cartilage
marrow space produced by osteoclast activity
blood vessel
marrow cells some of which become osteoblasts

CANCELLATE BONE

osteoblast building bone
osteocyte in bone
bone matrix
marrow space in spongy bone

DEVELOPMENT OF A LONG BONE

I. Cartilage.

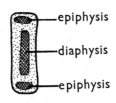

- epiphysis
- diaphysis
- epiphysis

II. Centres of ossification appear in the cartilage. Usually the diaphysis develops first and the epiphyses somewhat later.

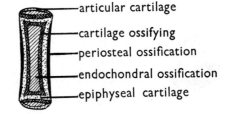

- articular cartilage
- cartilage ossifying
- periosteal ossification
- endochondral ossification
- epiphyseal cartilage

III. Endochondral ossification is the formation of bone from cartilage in the epiphyses and diaphysis. Periosteal ossification is the formation of bone from the periosteum surrounding the cartilage and the endochondral ossification. Epiphyseal and articular cartilages are retained.

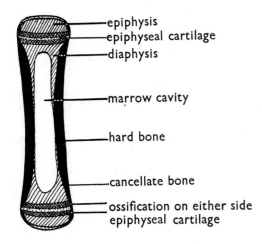

- epiphysis
- epiphyseal cartilage
- diaphysis
- marrow cavity
- hard bone
- cancellate bone
- ossification on either side epiphyseal cartilage

IV. Continuous growth of the epiphyseal cartilages with ossification on both sides of each of them produces increase in length. Periosteal ossification produces increase in thickness. A marrow cavity is excavated in the shaft.

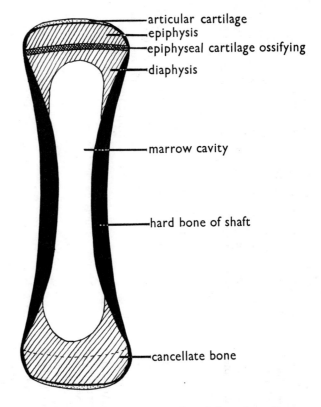

- articular cartilage
- epiphysis
- epiphyseal cartilage ossifying
- diaphysis
- marrow cavity
- hard bone of shaft
- cancellate bone

V. When growth in length is complete the epiphyseal cartilage ossifies and the epiphyses fuse with the diaphysis. The shaft is of hard bone but spongy bone remains in the ends. The marrow cavity is large and is filled with pulpy marrow.

THE FUNCTIONS OF THE SKELETON

The functions of the skeleton are:

1. SUPPORT. All the tissues except cartilage and bone are soft. Without the skeleton the body would be flabby and could not stand up. The arrangement of the bones gives shape to the body as a whole.

2. ATTACHMENT OF MUSCLES. The skeleton is jointed to allow movement. The movements are brought about by muscles which are attached to the bones and so pull them into different positions. The bones act as levers.

3. PROTECTION. The skeleton protects the more delicate parts of the body, e.g. the cranium protects the brain, the neural arches of the vertebral column surround the spinal cord, and the heart and lungs lie within the thoracic cage.

THE PARTS OF THE SKELETON

The skeleton may be considered in two sections: the **axial** skeleton which supports the parts on the main axis of the body, viz. the head, neck and trunk; and the **appendicular** skeleton which supports the appendages or limbs and gives them attachment to the rest of the body.
The bones are classified as long, short, flat and irregular, according to their shape.

I. THE AXIAL SKELETON is composed of the following parts:

SKULL—cranium 8 bones; face 14 bones; auditory ossicles 6 bones
HYOID BONE—1 bone
VERTEBRAL COLUMN—33 vertebrae but some of them fused so that there are usually 26 bones
STERNUM—3 bones
RIBS—12 pairs (24 bones)

II. THE APPENDICULAR SKELETON is composed of the following parts:

SHOULDER GIRDLE—2 scapulae and 2 clavicles
ARM BONES—1 humerus, 1 radius and 1 ulna in each arm
WRIST BONES—8 carpal bones in each wrist
HAND BONES—5 metacarpal bones in each hand
FINGER BONES—14 phalanges on each hand, 2 in each thumb and 3 in each of the other fingers
HIP GIRDLE—2 innominate bones each formed of an ilium, an ischium and a pubis
LEG BONES—1 femur, 1 tibia and 1 fibula in each leg
ANKLE AND FOOT BONES—7 tarsals and 5 metatarsals in each foot
TOE BONES—14 phalanges on each foot, 2 in each great toe and 3 in each of the other toes

THE SKULL

The skull consists of two parts, the **cranium** or brain-box and the **face**, and has three small bones enclosed in the cavity of each ear.

1. THE CRANIUM is a complete box formed by the following bones:

1 **occipital** bone at the back of the skull;
2 **parietal** bones forming the hind part of the roof of the skull;
1 **frontal** bone forming the front part of the roof of the skull, the forehead, and the upper parts of the orbits;
2 **temporal** bones at the sides, above and around the ears;
1 **sphenoid** bone at the base of the cranium, with wings on either side forming the temples;
1 **ethmoid** bone between the frontal and the sphenoid, forming the roof of the nasal cavities.

2. THE FACE is supported by fourteen bones:

2 **zygomatic** or **malar** bones in the cheeks;
2 **maxillae** forming the upper jaw, most of the side walls of the nose and front part of the hard palate;
2 **palatine** bones forming the rest of the hard palate and part of the side walls of the nose;
2 **lacrimal** bones, one in each eye socket or orbit;
2 **nasal** bones forming the bridge of the nose;
2 **turbinate** bones inside the nose;
1 **vomer** forming part of the nasal septum;
1 **mandible** forming the lower jaw.

skull
mandible
hyoid bone
vertebral column
sternum
ribs
clavicle
scapula
humerus
radius
ulna
carpals
metacarpals
phalanges
innominate bone
femur
patella
tibia
fibula
tarsals
metatarsals
phalanges

The arrangement of the parts of the skeleton

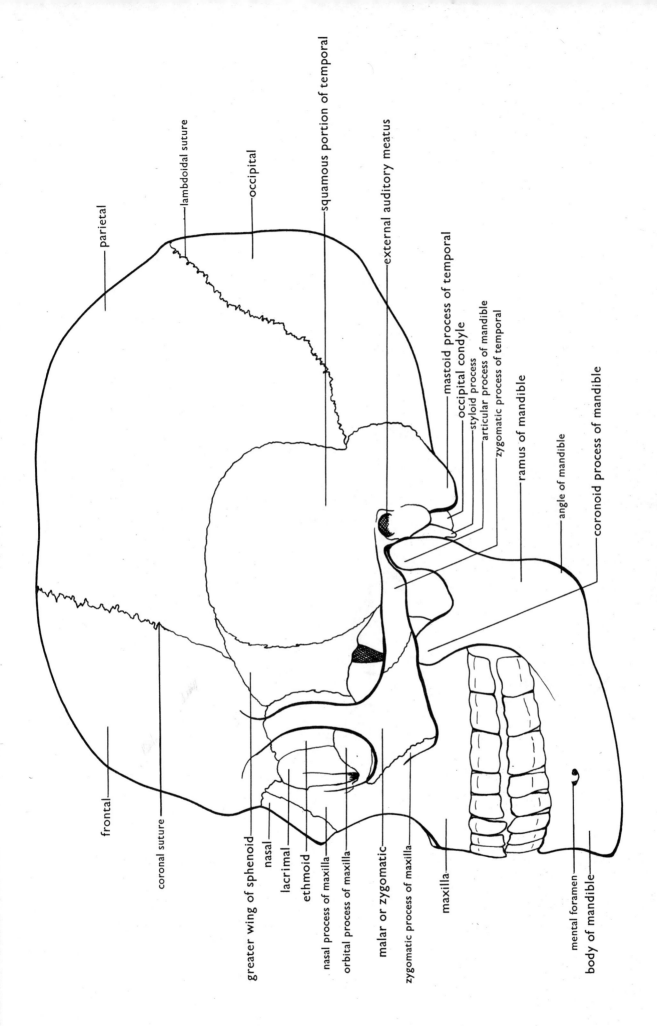

parietal

lambdoidal suture

occipital

squamous portion of temporal

external auditory meatus

mastoid process of temporal

occipital condyle

styloid process

articular process of mandible

zygomatic process of temporal

ramus of mandible

angle of mandible

coronoid process of mandible

frontal

coronal suture

greater wing of sphenoid

nasal

lacrimal

ethmoid

nasal process of maxilla

orbital process of maxilla

malar or zygomatic

zygomatic process of maxilla

maxilla

mental foramen

body of mandible

Skull—*lateral view*

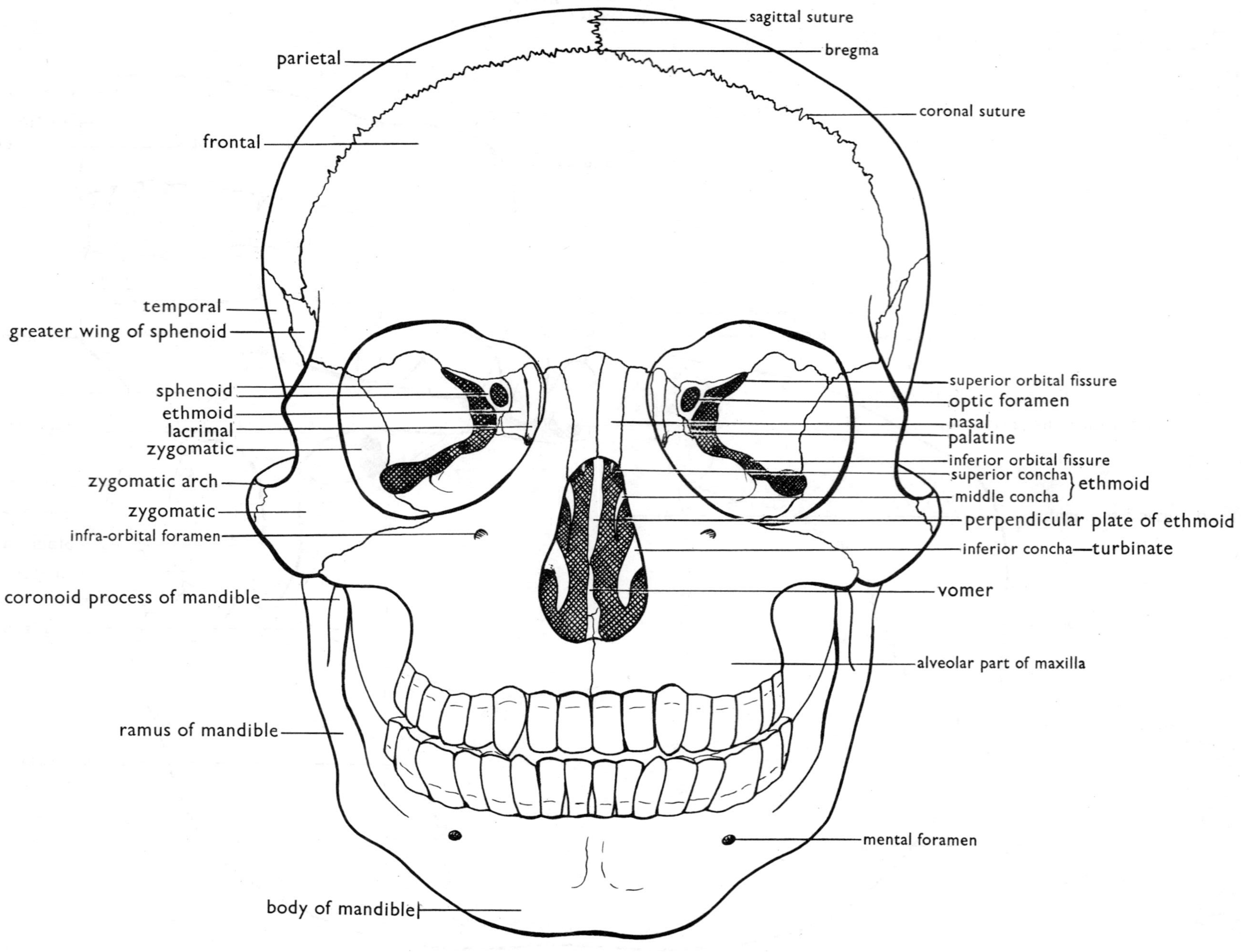

6

Skull—*frontal view*

sagittal suture

bregma

coronal suture

parietal

frontal

temporal

greater wing of sphenoid

sphenoid

ethmoid

lacrimal

zygomatic

zygomatic arch

zygomatic

infra-orbital foramen

coronoid process of mandible

ramus of mandible

body of mandible

superior orbital fissure

optic foramen

nasal

palatine

inferior orbital fissure

superior concha } ethmoid

middle concha

perpendicular plate of ethmoid

inferior concha—turbinate

vomer

alveolar part of maxilla

mental foramen

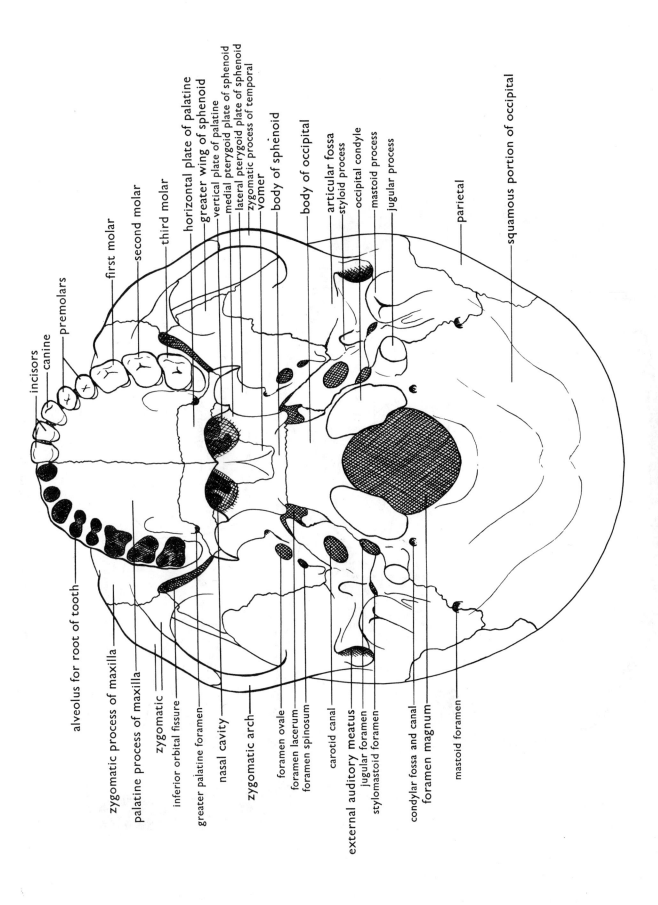

Skull—*external view of the base*

incisors
canine
premolars
first molar
second molar
third molar
horizontal plate of palatine
greater wing of sphenoid
vertical plate of palatine
medial pterygoid plate of sphenoid
lateral pterygoid plate of sphenoid
zygomatic process of temporal
vomer
body of sphenoid
body of occipital
articular fossa
styloid process
occipital condyle
mastoid process
jugular process
parietal
squamous portion of occipital

alveolus for root of tooth
zygomatic process of maxilla
palatine process of maxilla
zygomatic
inferior orbital fissure
greater palatine foramen
nasal cavity
zygomatic arch
foramen ovale
foramen lacerum
foramen spinosum
carotid canal
external auditory meatus
jugular foramen
stylomastoid foramen
condylar fossa and canal
foramen magnum
mastoid foramen

8

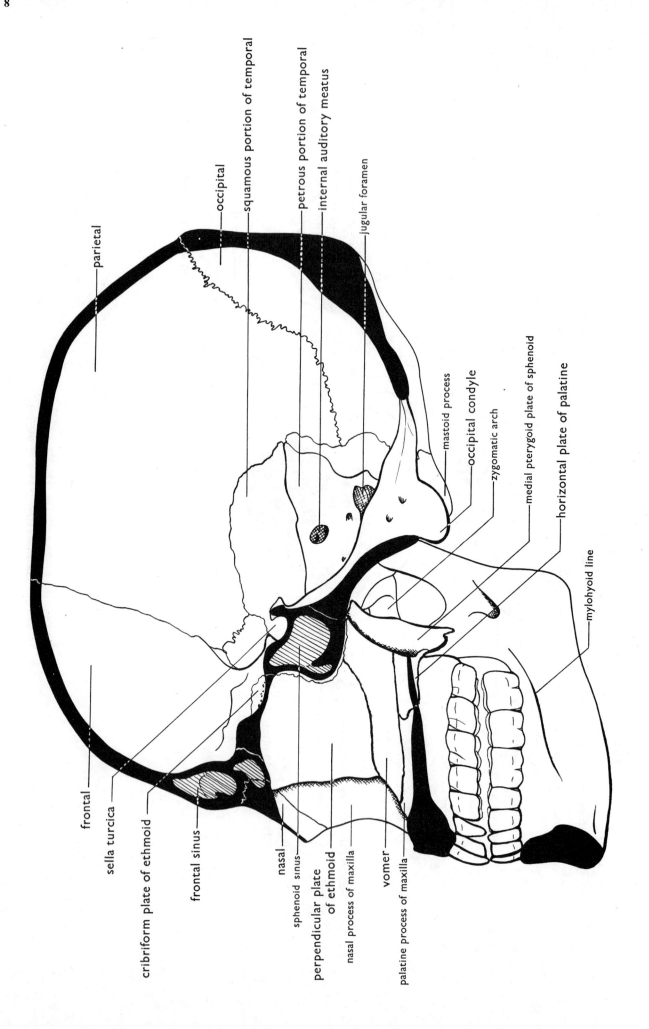

parietal

occipital

squamous portion of temporal

petrous portion of temporal

internal auditory meatus

jugular foramen

mastoid process

occipital condyle

zygomatic arch

medial pterygoid plate of sphenoid

horizontal plate of palatine

mylohyoid line

frontal

sella turcica

cribriform plate of ethmoid

frontal sinus

nasal

sphenoid sinus

perpendicular plate of ethmoid

nasal process of maxilla

vomer

palatine process of maxilla

Skull—*vertical section slightly to the left of the mid-line*

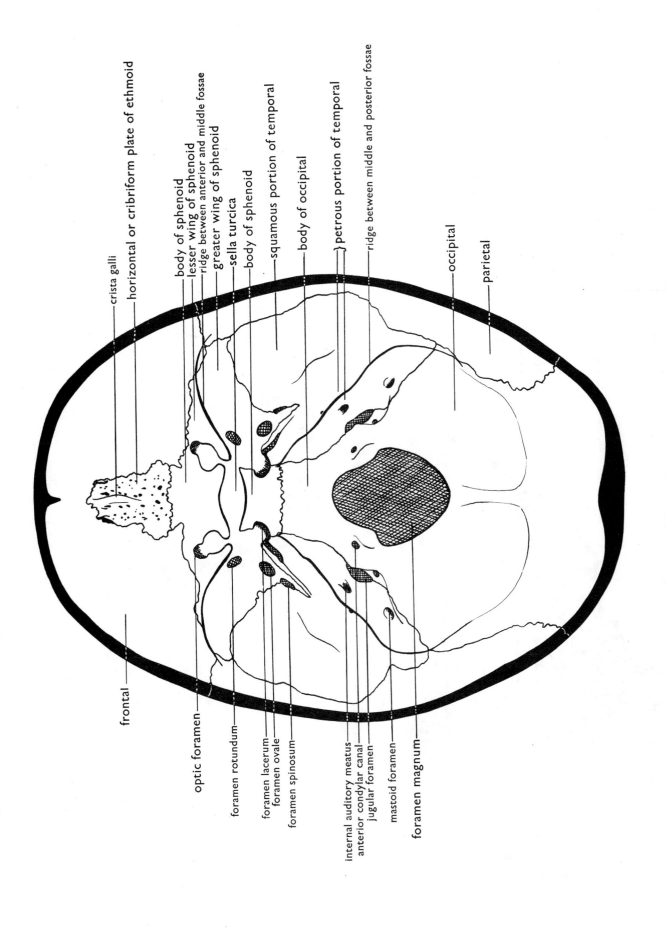

crista galli

horizontal or cribriform plate of ethmoid

body of sphenoid

lesser wing of sphenoid

ridge between anterior and middle fossae

greater wing of sphenoid

sella turcica

body of sphenoid

squamous portion of temporal

body of occipital

petrous portion of temporal

ridge between middle and posterior fossae

occipital

parietal

frontal

optic foramen

foramen rotundum

foramen lacerum

foramen ovale

foramen spinosum

internal auditory meatus

anterior condylar canal

jugular foramen

mastoid foramen

foramen magnum

Skull—*view of base with crown removed*

THE SINUSES

The paranasal sinuses are air-filled spaces in the frontal, sphenoid, ethmoid and maxillary bones. They communicate with the nasal air cavities and are lined with mucous membrane, continuous with the nasal mucosa. The maxillary sinuses are very large and are also known as the antra of Highmore.

The mastoid antra or air cells are sinuses in the mastoid portion of each temporal bone. They communicate with the tympanic cavities (see page 66).

THE AUDITORY OSSICLES

The auditory ossicles lie in the middle-ear cavity. They are a chain of three small bones stretching between the tympanic membrane and the fenestra ovalis (see THE EAR, page 67). They are called the **malleus**, the **incus** and the **stapes.**

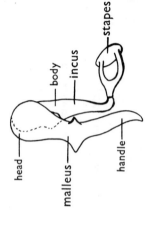

Auditory ossicles

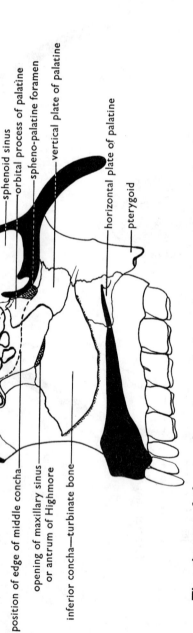

The sinuses of the nasal region and the nasal cavity—*superior and middle conchae removed*

frontal sinus — ethmoid sinuses — position of edge of superior concha — position of edge of middle concha — opening of maxillary sinus or antrum of Highmore — inferior concha—turbinate bone — sphenoid sinus — orbital process of palatine — spheno-palatine foramen — vertical plate of palatine — horizontal plate of palatine — pterygoid

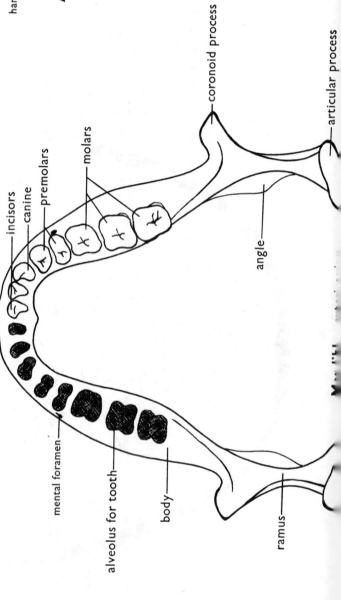

incisors — canine — premolars — molars — coronoid process — articular process — angle — ramus — body — alveolus for tooth — mental foramen

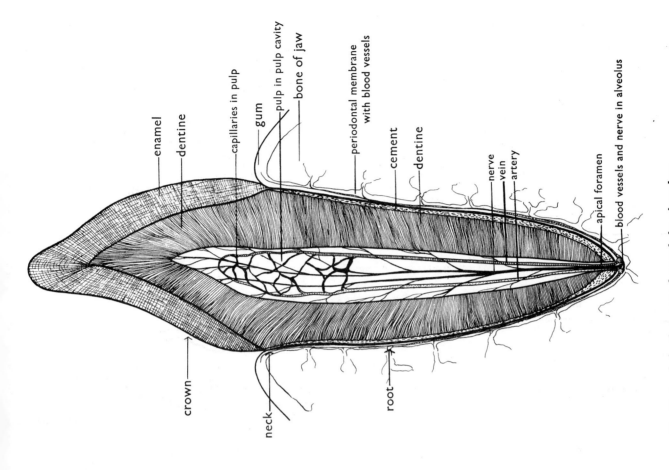

enamel
dentine
capillaries in pulp
gum
pulp in pulp cavity
bone of jaw
periodontal membrane with blood vessels
cement
dentine
nerve
vein
artery
apical foramen
blood vessels and nerve in alveolus
crown
neck
root

Section of single rooted tooth in alveolus—
distribution of blood vessels and nerves shown diagrammatically

THE TEETH

The teeth are set in sockets in the jaw-bones called **alveoli** (see pages 7 and 10). Each tooth has a **crown** above the gum, a **neck** at gum-level and a **root** embedded in the bone. The bulk of the tooth is made of a bone-like substance called **dentine**, formed by the activity of **odontoblasts** and hardened by deposits of calcium phosphate. The crown is capped with very hard, non-living **enamel** formed in the tooth-bud by **ameloblasts**. The root is invested in a thin layer of **cement** and joined to the jaw-bone by the **periodontal membrane** in which there are blood-vessels. The dentine is served by nerves and blood-vessels which lie amongst spongy pulp cells in the central pulp cavity.

Two sets of teeth are developed during life. The tooth rudiments formed from the **dental lamina** are present in the jaws before birth, but erupt gradually as the jaws grow big enough to accommodate them. The temporary or **milk dentition** begins to appear at about five months and is usually complete by twenty months. This dentition consists of twenty teeth—2 incisors, 1 canine and 2 molars in each half of each jaw. (Though placed in front of the molars, the canines usually erupt later than the first molars.) The **permanent dentition** consists of thirty-two teeth. Twenty of these—2 incisors, 1 canine and 2 premolars in each half of each jaw—replace the milk teeth when these are shed between the ages of seven and eleven and are larger than their precursors. In addition to these replacement teeth the permanent dentition has three groups of non-replacement teeth—the six-year-old, twelve-year-old and eighteen-year-old molars respectively. The last are also known as the wisdom teeth and are often very late in erupting.

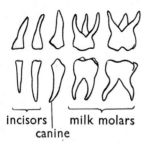

incisors | milk molars
canine

Milk dentition

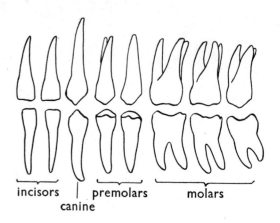

incisors | premolars   molars
canine

Permanent dentition

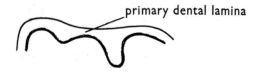

primary dental lamina

I. The foetal gum forms, continuous with the lip.

lip
labial groove

dental groove
dental lamina
rudiment of enamel organ
rudiment of dental papilla
rudiment of dental sac

II. The dental lamina forms as a fold of the foetal gum.
    Buds arise on the outer side of the lamina, each bud
    becoming an enamel organ. Under the enamel organ
    connective tissue forms the dental papilla.

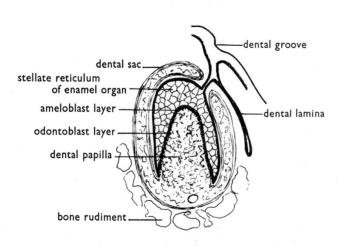

dental groove
dental sac
stellate reticulum
   of enamel organ
ameloblast layer
dental lamina
odontoblast layer
dental papilla

bone rudiment

III. The enamel organ develops a distinct ameloblast
     layer and stellate reticulum. The dental papilla develops
     an odontoblast layer. Connective tissue around the
     tooth rudiment becomes the dental sac.

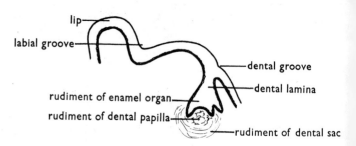

dental sac
enamel organ
ameloblasts
enamel
dentine
odontoblasts
pulp
dental lamina
bud of enamel organ

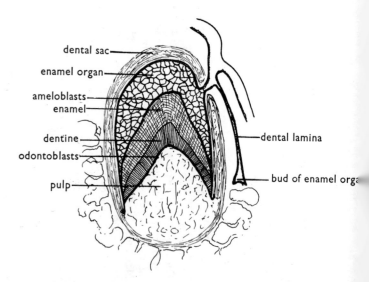

Stages in the development of teeth

IV. The ameloblasts of the enamel organ lay down enamel
    and the odontoblasts of the dental papilla produce
    dentine matrix which gradually becomes calcified.

    The dental lamina continues to grow and produces
    a second series of buds from which the second set of
    teeth develop later.

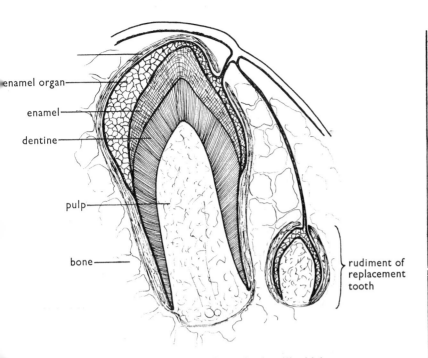

enamel organ
enamel
dentine
pulp
bone
rudiment of replacement tooth

V. The tooth is ready to erupt. The pulp cavity is still widely open at the base. The rudiment of the replacement tooth is formed.

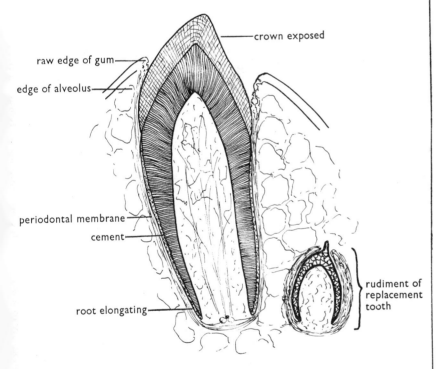

crown exposed
raw edge of gum
edge of alveolus
periodontal membrane
cement
root elongating
rudiment of replacement tooth

VI. The tooth erupts by growth of the root accompanied by rupture of the gum, dental sac and enamel organ and resorption of some bone around the edges of the alveolus. The inner layer of the dental sac forms cement while the outer layer becomes the periodontal membrane

Stages in the development of teeth—*continued*

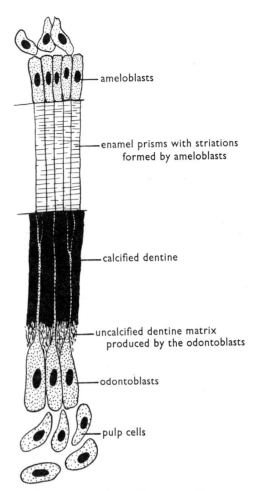

ameloblasts
enamel prisms with striations formed by ameloblasts
calcified dentine
uncalcified dentine matrix produced by the odontoblasts
odontoblasts
pulp cells

Diagram to show the growth of enamel and dentine

THE HYOID BONE

The hyoid bone lies at the base of the tongue. It has a **body** and two pairs of horns or **cornua.**

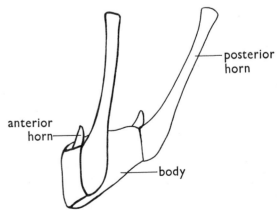

posterior horn
anterior horn
body

Hyoid bone—*postero-lateral view*

7 cervical vertebrae

12 dorsal or thoracic vertebrae

5 lumbar vertebrae

sacrum of 5 sacral vertebrae

coccyx of 4 coccygeal vertebrae

cervical curvature

thoracic curvature

lumbar curvature

sacral curvature

Vertebral column—*lateral view*

THE VERTEBRAL COLUMN

The vertebral column is composed of thirty-three vertebrae some of which are fused so that there are only twenty-six bones. It has the following regions:

CERVICAL REGION in the neck—7 vertebrae.
THORACIC OR DORSAL REGION in the thorax—12 vertebrae.
LUMBAR REGION in the small of the back—5 vertebrae.
SACRAL REGION in the pelvis—5 vertebrae fused to form the sacrum.
COCCYGEAL REGION below the sacrum—4 vertebrae fused to form the coccyx.

The column shows curvatures in the cervical, thoracic, lumbar and sacral regions. The **thoracic** and **sacral curvatures** are primary and are present before the infant is born. The **cervical** and **lumbar curvatures** are secondary. The former develops when the infant lifts its head and the latter when it starts to walk.

THE VERTEBRAE

A typical vertebra has a **body**, a **neural arch** and **seven processes.**
The body is approximately cylindrical with flattened upper and lower surfaces, which articulate with adjacent vertebrae through **intervertebral discs** (see page 28). The neural arch is formed of two stalk-like **pedicles** and two flattened **laminae.** The processes are attached to the neural arch thus:

a **spinous process** at the junction of the two laminae;
two **transverse processes**, one on either side, at the junction of each pedicle with the corresponding lamina;
two **superior articular processes** and two **inferior articular processes** on the upper and lower edges of the laminae respectively.

The articular processes are slanted to fit the corresponding processes of the adjacent vertebrae and form gliding joints (see page 28).
The neural arch encloses a canal called the **vertebral foramen** through which runs the spinal cord. **Intervertebral notches** between the pedicles of adjacent vertebrae permit the emergence of spinal nerves (see page 60).

The CERVICAL vertebrae can be recognised by the possession of a canal called a **foramen transversarium** in each transverse process. The second to sixth vertebrae have cloven spinous processes.

The first two cervical vertebrae, the **atlas** and the **axis**, are specialised to support and allow free movement of the head. The atlas has no body, no spinous process and no articular processes. In place of the body is a socket for the odontoid peg of the axis. On either side of this socket lie concave facets for articulation with the skull and with the axis and there is a further facet on the floor of the socket itself. In life the canal of the atlas is traversed by a band of ligament designed to hold the odontoid peg in place. The axis has a large projecting process, the **odontoid peg**, attached to the superior surface of the body. On either side of this is a convex facet for articulation with the atlas, but there are no superior articular processes on the neural arch. On the anterior surface of the odontoid peg is a curved facet for articulation with the socket of the atlas. Nodding movement takes place between the skull and the atlas, while turning of the head takes place between the atlas and the axis.

The THORACIC VERTEBRAE can be recognised by the facets for articulation of the ribs. The first ten thoracic vertebrae have two pairs of demi-facets on the body because the heads of the second to tenth pairs of ribs overlap on to the vertebrae above those to which they belong, but the first and the last two pairs of ribs articulate directly with the corresponding vertebrae. The transverse processes of the first ten thoracic vertebrae bear facets for the tubercles of the ribs.
The LUMBAR VERTEBRAE are larger and stronger than the other vertebrae.
The SACRUM is formed of five vertebrae whose bodies and transverse processes are fused. The junctions can be identified and there are foramina between them for the emergence of nerves. The spinous processes are reduced. The first sacral vertebra only has free articular processes.
The COCCYX forms a small appendix to the sacrum. It consists of four vertebrae which are

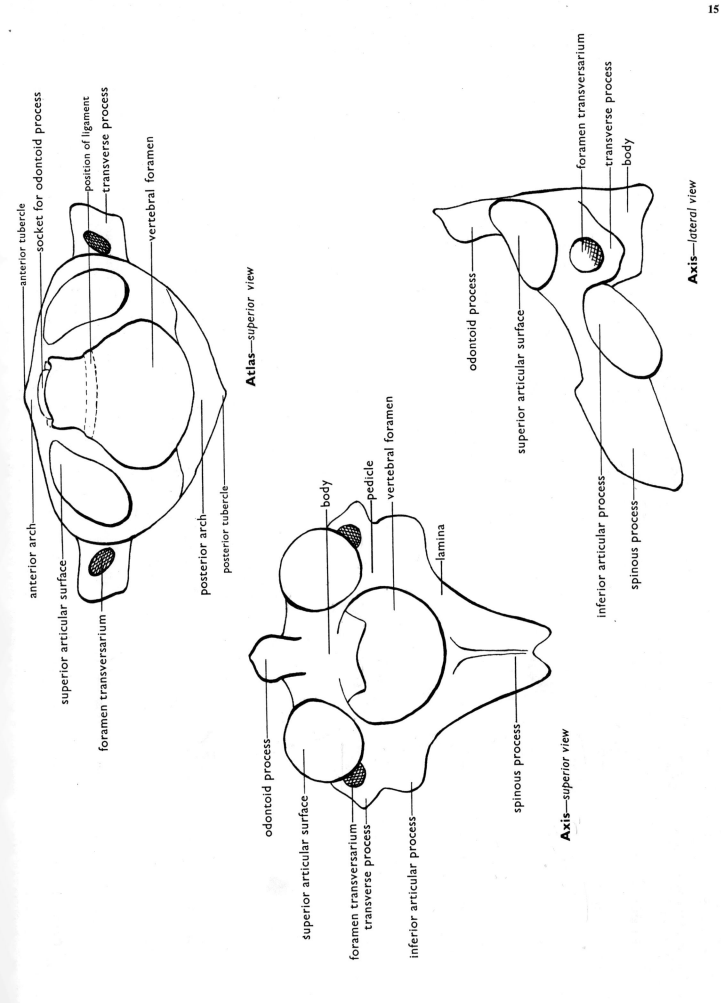

Atlas—*superior view*

anterior tubercle

socket for odontoid process

position of ligament

transverse process

vertebral foramen

anterior arch

superior articular surface

foramen transversarium

posterior arch

posterior tubercle

Axis—*superior view*

body

pedicle

vertebral foramen

lamina

odontoid process

superior articular surface

foramen transversarium

transverse process

inferior articular process

spinous process

Axis—*lateral view*

foramen transversarium

transverse process

body

odontoid process

superior articular surface

inferior articular process

spinous process

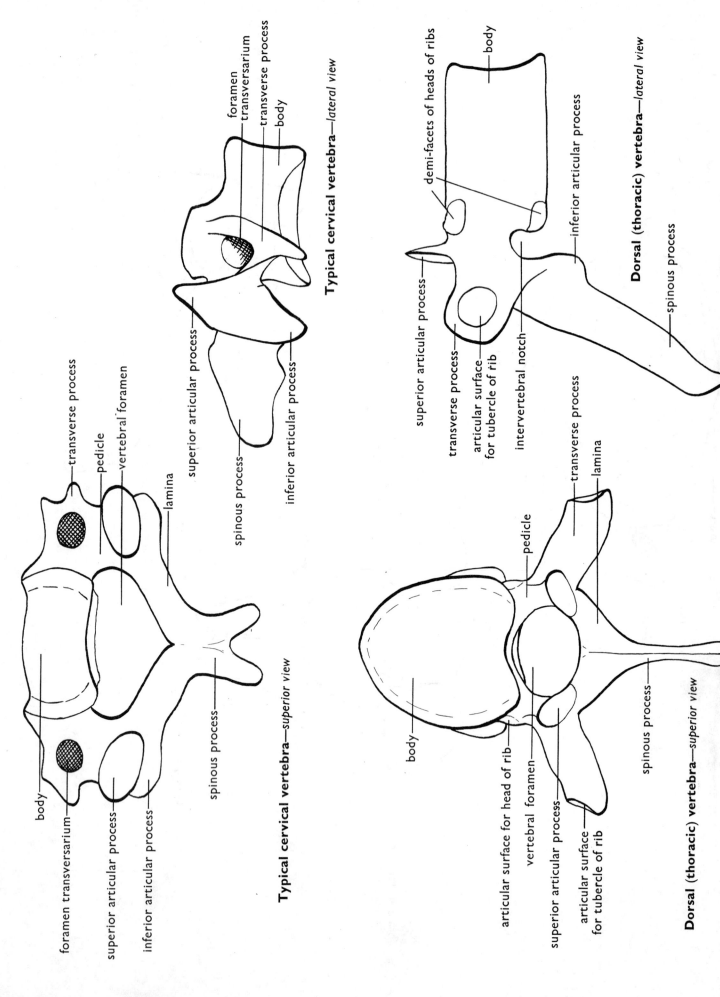

Typical cervical vertebra—*lateral view*

foramen transversarium
transverse process
body

transverse process
pedicle
vertebral foramen
lamina
superior articular process
spinous process
inferior articular process

body
foramen transversarium
superior articular process
inferior articular process

Typical cervical vertebra—*superior view*

demi-facets of heads of ribs
body

superior articular process
inferior articular process
spinous process

Dorsal (thoracic) vertebra—*lateral view*

superior articular process
transverse process
articular surface for tubercle of rib
intervertebral notch

pedicle
transverse process
lamina

body
articular surface for head of rib
vertebral foramen
superior articular process
articular surface for tubercle of rib
spinous process

Dorsal (thoracic) vertebra—*superior view*

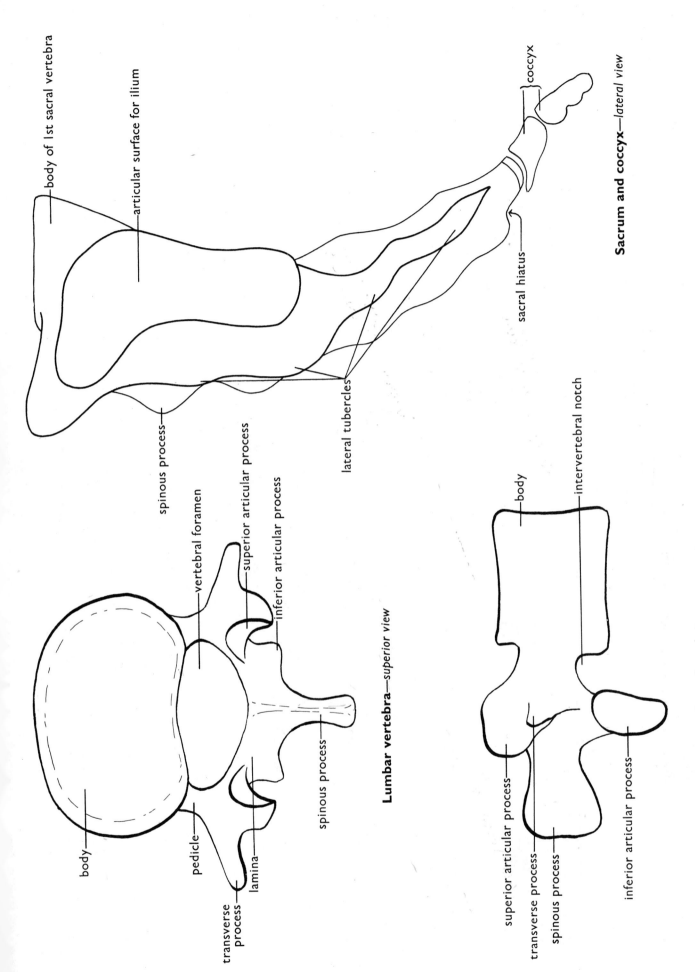

body of 1st sacral vertebra

articular surface for ilium

coccyx

Sacrum and coccyx—*lateral view*

sacral hiatus

spinous process

lateral tubercles

vertebral foramen

superior articular process

inferior articular process

intervertebral notch

body

Lumbar vertebra—*superior view*

body

pedicle

transverse process

lamina

spinous process

superior articular process

transverse process

spinous process

inferior articular process

Lumbar vertebra—*lateral view*

18

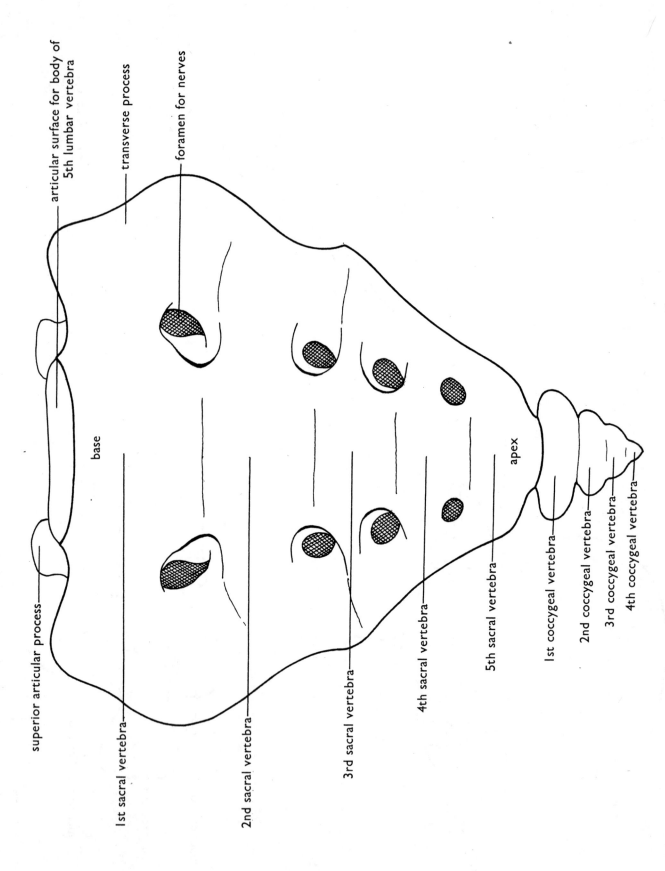

superior articular process

articular surface for body of 5th lumbar vertebra

transverse process

foramen for nerves

base

1st sacral vertebra

2nd sacral vertebra

3rd sacral vertebra

4th sacral vertebra

5th sacral vertebra

apex

1st coccygeal vertebra

2nd coccygeal vertebra

3rd coccygeal vertebra

4th coccygeal vertebra

Sacrum and coccyx—*ventral view*

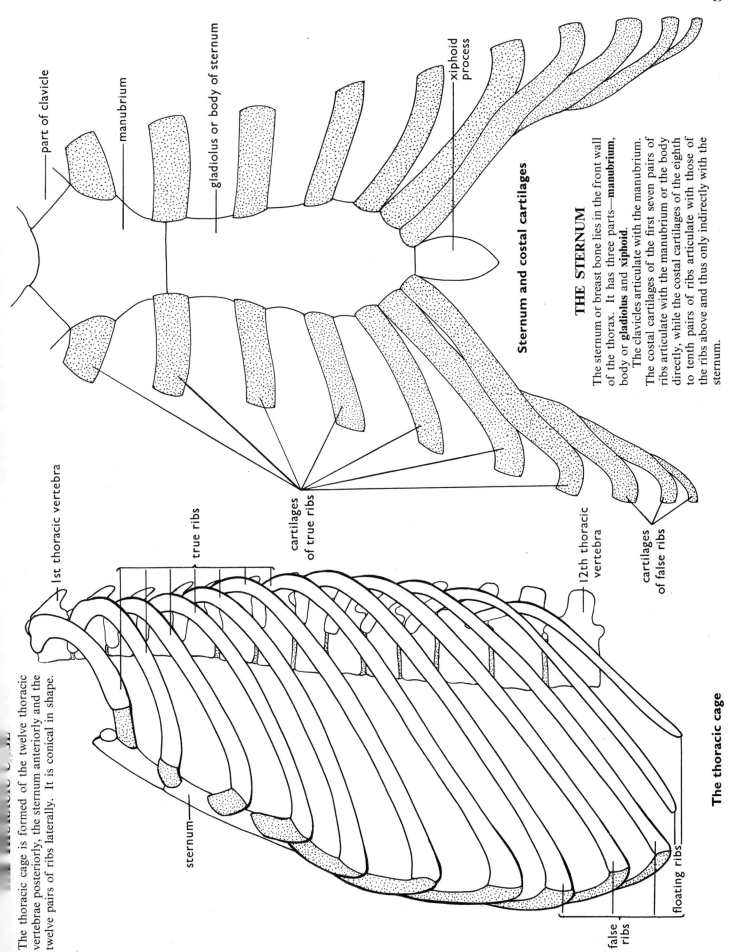

19

The thoracic cage is formed of the twelve thoracic vertebrae posteriorly, the sternum anteriorly and the twelve pairs of ribs laterally. It is conical in shape.

part of clavicle

manubrium

gladiolus or body of sternum

xiphoid process

Sternum and costal cartilages

THE STERNUM

The sternum or breast bone lies in the front wall of the thorax. It has three parts—**manubrium,** body or **gladiolus** and **xiphoid.**

The clavicles articulate with the manubrium.

The costal cartilages of the first seven pairs of ribs articulate with the manubrium or the body directly, while the costal cartilages of the eighth to tenth pairs of ribs articulate with those of the ribs above and thus only indirectly with the sternum.

1st thoracic vertebra

true ribs

cartilages of true ribs

12th thoracic vertebra

cartilages of false ribs

sternum

false ribs

floating ribs

The thoracic cage

THE RIBS

There are twelve pairs of ribs. Each rib typically has a **head**, which articulates with the bodies of two vertebrae, a **tubercle** which articulates with the transverse process of a vertebra, and a **shaft** which curves round the side wall of the thorax. The last two pairs of ribs have no tubercles.

The anterior ends of the first ten pairs of ribs articulate with costal cartilages, while the last two pairs of ribs are free or floating ribs. The seven pairs of ribs whose cartilages articulate directly with the sternum are called true ribs, while the five pairs of ribs with indirect or with no attachment to the sternum are called false ribs.

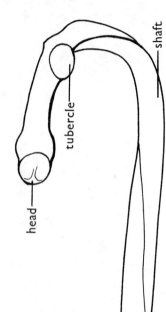

head

tubercle

shaft.

Rib

position of attachment of rib cartilage

---

acromion process

coracoid process

glenoid cavity

superior angle

spine

supraspinous fossa

infraspinous fossa

vertebral border

axillary border

inferior angle

Right scapula, dorsal view

THE SHOULDER GIRDLE

The shoulder girdle consists of two **scapulae** or shoulder blades and two **clavicles** or collar bones. The clavicles articulate with the sternum so that the girdle forms an incomplete ring around the upper part of the thorax.

sternal end

shaft

acromial end

Right clavicle, anterior view

21

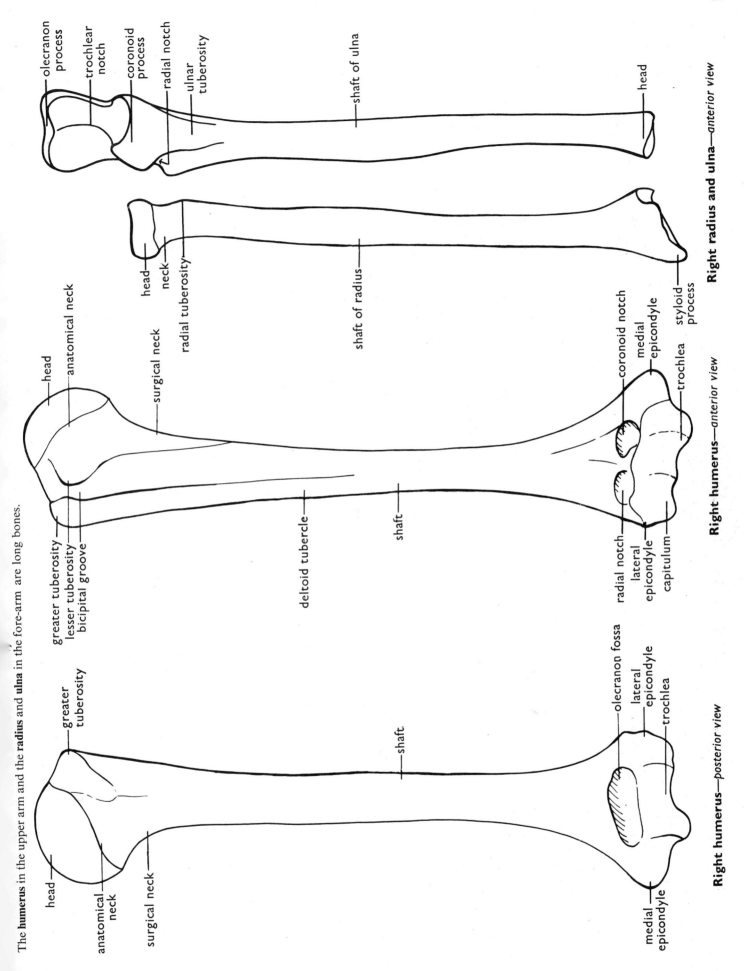

The **humerus** in the upper arm and the **radius** and **ulna** in the fore-arm are long bones.

Right radius and ulna—*anterior view*

olecranon process
trochlear notch
coronoid process
radial notch
ulnar tuberosity
shaft of ulna
head

head
neck
radial tuberosity
shaft of radius

head
anatomical neck
surgical neck

greater tuberosity
lesser tuberosity
bicipital groove

deltoid tubercle
shaft

coronoid notch
medial epicondyle
trochlea

radial notch
lateral epicondyle
capitulum

Right humerus—*anterior view*

greater tuberosity

shaft

olecranon fossa
lateral epicondyle
trochlea

head
anatomical neck
surgical neck

medial epicondyle

Right humerus—*posterior view*

22

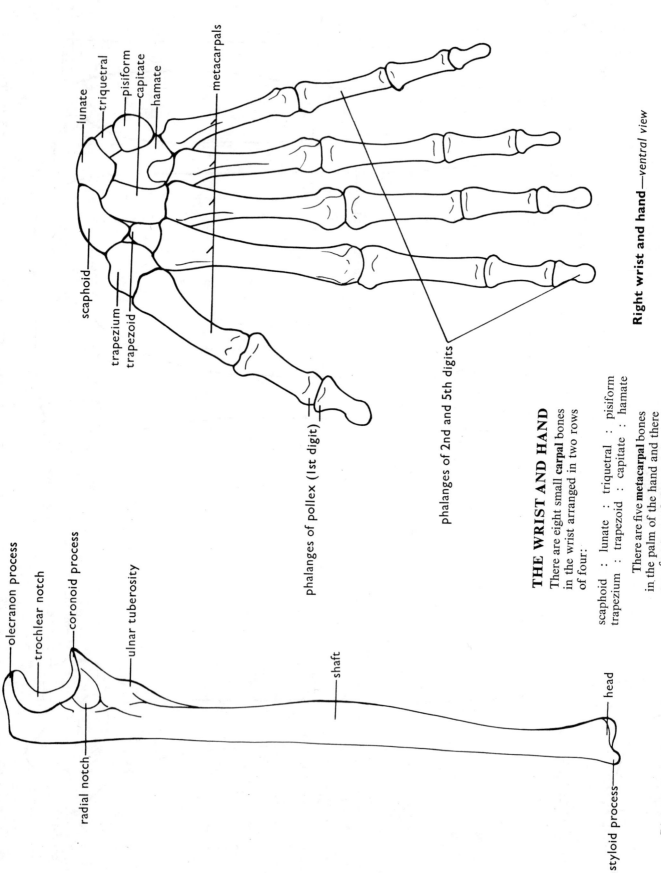

lunate
triquetral
pisiform
capitate
hamate

metacarpals

scaphoid

trapezium
trapezoid

phalanges of pollex (1st digit)

phalanges of 2nd and 5th digits

Right wrist and hand—*ventral view*

olecranon process
trochlear notch
coronoid process

ulnar tuberosity

radial notch

shaft

head

styloid process

Right ulna—*lateral view*

THE WRIST AND HAND

There are eight small **carpal** bones in the wrist arranged in two rows of four:

scaphoid : lunate : triquetral : pisiform
trapezium : trapezoid : capitate : hamate

There are five **metacarpal** bones in the palm of the hand and there are fourteen **phalanges**, two of which are in the pollex or thumb and three in each of the other digits.

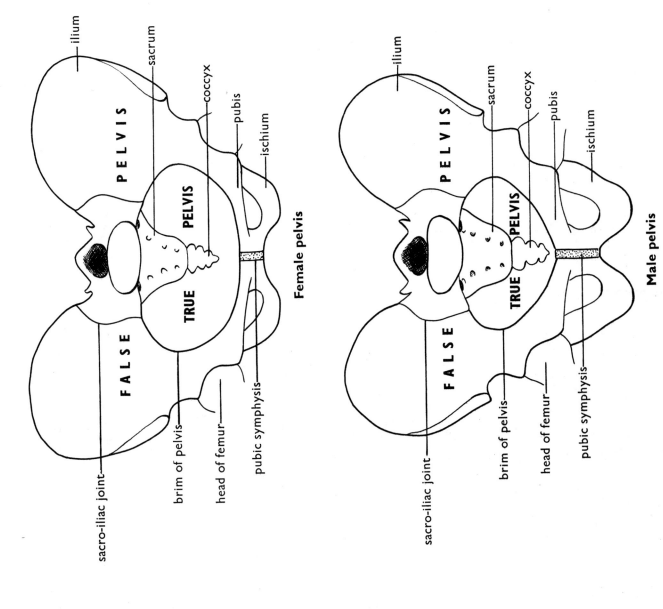

Female pelvis

Male pelvis

THE HIP GIRDLE

The hip girdle is formed of two large **innominate** bones which meet one another anteriorly at the **pubic symphysis** and articulate with the sacrum posteriorly to form a firm ring of bone. The innominate bones with the sacrum and coccyx form the **pelvis** which surrounds the pelvic cavity. The pelvis of the female is wider and shallower than that of the male.

Each innominate bone is formed by the fusion of three parts, an **ilium**, an **ischium** and a **pubis**. At the junction of these is a socket, the **acetabulum**, for the head of the femur.

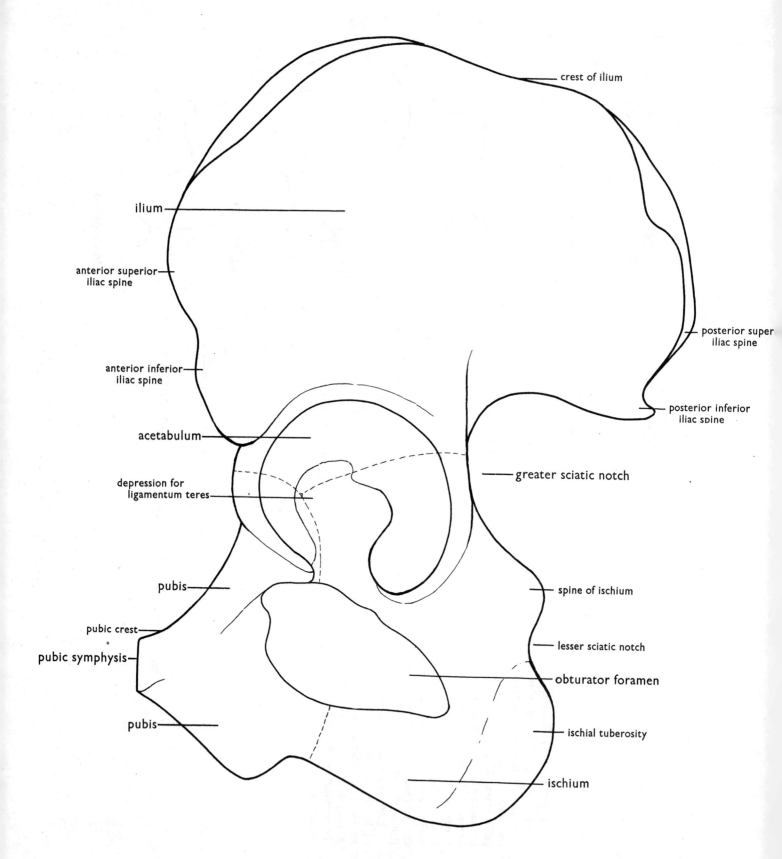

crest of ilium

ilium

anterior superior iliac spine

posterior super iliac spine

anterior inferior iliac spine

posterior inferior iliac spine

acetabulum

greater sciatic notch

depression for ligamentum teres

pubis

spine of ischium

pubic crest

lesser sciatic notch

pubic symphysis

obturator foramen

ischial tuberosity

pubis

ischium

Left innominate bone—*lateral view*

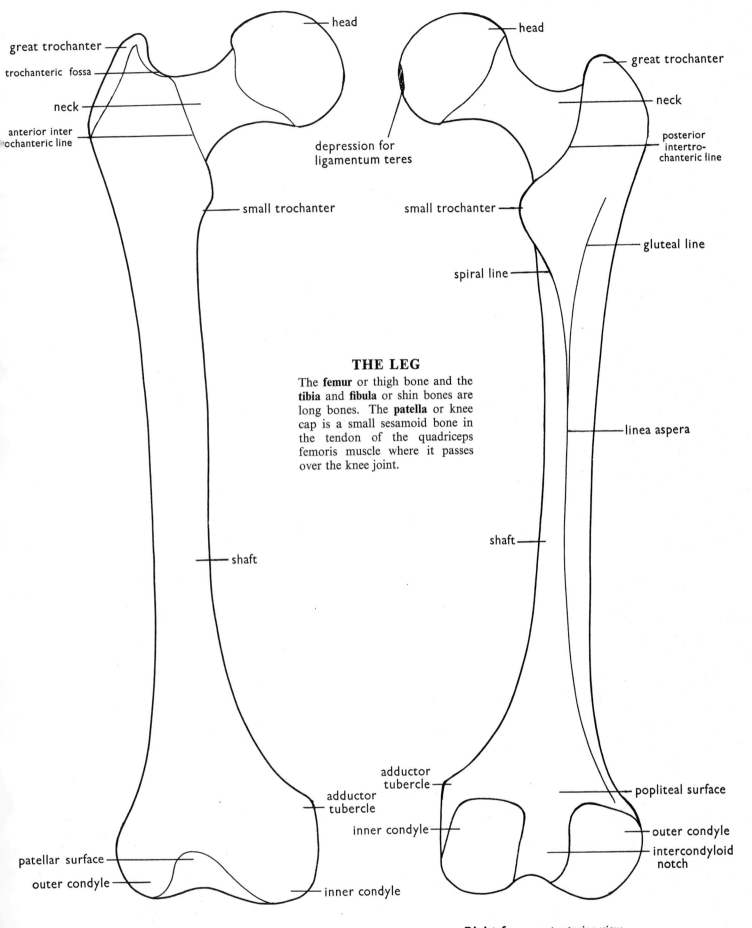

great trochanter

trochanteric fossa

neck

anterior inter
rochanteric line

head

head

great trochanter

neck

depression for
ligamentum teres

posterior
intertro-
chanteric line

small trochanter

small trochanter

gluteal line

spiral line

THE LEG

The **femur** or thigh bone and the **tibia** and **fibula** or shin bones are long bones. The **patella** or knee cap is a small sesamoid bone in the tendon of the quadriceps femoris muscle where it passes over the knee joint.

linea aspera

shaft

shaft

adductor
tubercle

adductor
tubercle

popliteal surface

adductor
tubercle

inner condyle

outer condyle

patellar surface

intercondyloid
notch

outer condyle

inner condyle

Right femur—*anterior view*

Right femur—*posterior view*

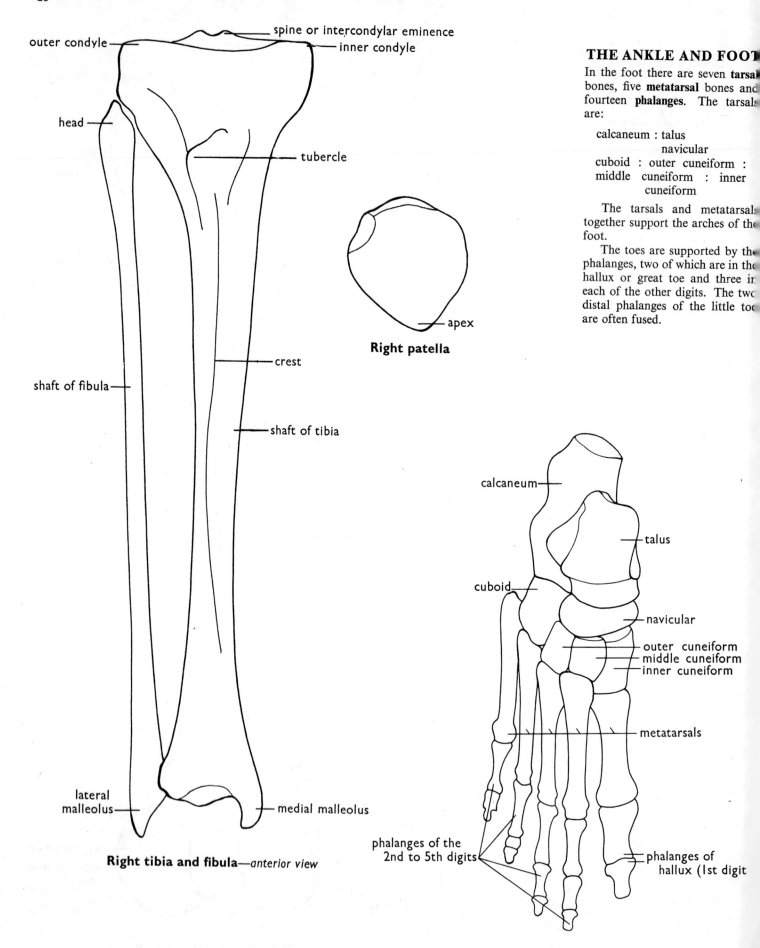

outer condyle

spine or intercondylar eminence

inner condyle

head

tubercle

shaft of fibula

crest

shaft of tibia

lateral malleolus

medial malleolus

Right tibia and fibula—*anterior view*

apex

Right patella

THE ANKLE AND FOOT

In the foot there are seven **tarsal** bones, five **metatarsal** bones and fourteen **phalanges**. The tarsals are:

calcaneum : talus
navicular
cuboid : outer cuneiform :
middle cuneiform : inner cuneiform

The tarsals and metatarsals together support the arches of the foot.

The toes are supported by the phalanges, two of which are in the hallux or great toe and three in each of the other digits. The two distal phalanges of the little toe are often fused.

calcaneum

talus

cuboid

navicular

outer cuneiform
middle cuneiform
inner cuneiform

metatarsals

phalanges of the 2nd to 5th digits

phalanges of hallux (1st digit

Right foot—*dorsal view*

THE JOINTS

Wherever one bone or cartilage meets another there is a joint. There are more joints in the child than in the adult because as growth proceeds some of the bones fuse together—e.g. the ilium, ischium and pubis to form the innominate bone; the two halves of the infant frontal bone, and of the infant mandible; the five sacral vertebrae and the four coccygeal vertebrae.

Joints are classified according to the amount of movement possible between the articulating surfaces.

SYNARTHROSES are fixed joints at which there is no movement. The articular surfaces are joined by tough fibrous tissue. Often the edges of the bones are dovetailed into one another as in the sutures of the skull.

AMPHIARTHROSES are joints at which slight movement is possible. A pad of cartilage lies between the bone surfaces, and there is a fibrous capsule to hold the bones and cartilage in place. The cartilages of such joints also act as shock absorbers (e.g. the intervertebral discs between the bodies of the vertebrae).

DIARTHROSES or SYNOVIAL JOINTS are known as freely movable joints, though at some of them the movement is restricted by the shape of the articulating surfaces. A synovial joint has a fluid-filled cavity between articular surfaces which are covered by articular cartilage. The fluid, known as synovial fluid, is a form of lymph produced by the synovial membrane which lines the cavity except for the actual articular surfaces and covers any ligaments or tendons which pass through the joint. Synovial fluid acts as a lubricant.

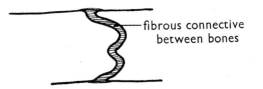

Synarthrosis—*fibrous joint*

- fibrous connective between bones

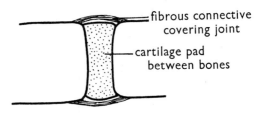

Amphiarthrosis—*cartilaginous joint*

- fibrous connective covering joint
- cartilage pad between bones

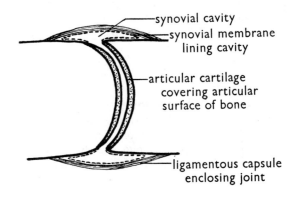

Diarthrosis—*synovial joint*

- synovial cavity
- synovial membrane lining cavity
- articular cartilage covering articular surface of bone
- ligamentous capsule enclosing joint

The **movements** possible at synovial joints are:

ANGULAR — flexion: decreasing the angle between two bones;
— extension: increasing the angle between two bones;
— abduction: moving the part away from the mid-line;
— adduction: bringing the part towards the mid-line.

ROTARY — rotation: turning upon an axis;
— circumduction: moving of the extremity of the part round in a circle so that the whole part inscribes a cone.

GLIDING — one part slides on another.

Gliding movement

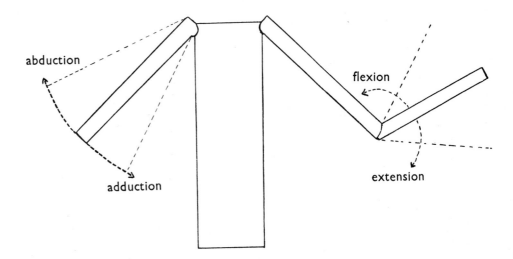

Angular movement

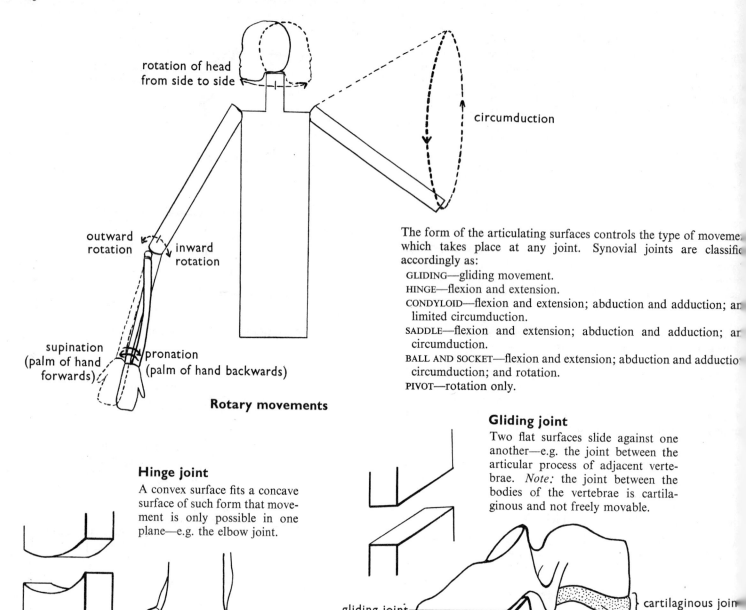

rotation of head from side to side

circumduction

outward rotation

inward rotation

supination (palm of hand forwards)

pronation (palm of hand backwards)

Rotary movements

The form of the articulating surfaces controls the type of movement which takes place at any joint. Synovial joints are classified accordingly as:

GLIDING—gliding movement.

HINGE—flexion and extension.

CONDYLOID—flexion and extension; abduction and adduction; and limited circumduction.

SADDLE—flexion and extension; abduction and adduction; and circumduction.

BALL AND SOCKET—flexion and extension; abduction and adduction; circumduction; and rotation.

PIVOT—rotation only.

Hinge joint

A convex surface fits a concave surface of such form that movement is only possible in one plane—e.g. the elbow joint.

humerus

trochlear notch

olecranon process

ulna

Hinge joint

Gliding joint

Two flat surfaces slide against one another—e.g. the joint between the articular process of adjacent vertebrae. *Note:* the joint between the bodies of the vertebrae is cartilaginous and not freely movable.

gliding joint

cartilaginous joint

intervertebral disc

intervertebral notch

Gliding joint

Condyloid joint

A convex surface fits a concave surface. The radii of curvature are not the same in all planes. Movement is angular in two planes with slight circumduction—e.g. the wrist joint.

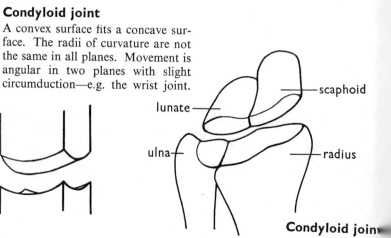

lunate

scaphoid

ulna

radius

Condyloid joint

Saddle joint

A concavo-convex surface fits into a convexo-concave surface. Angular movements and circumduction can be performed freely, but rotation is impossible—e.g. carpo-metacarpal joint of the thumb.

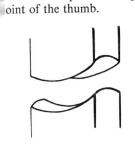 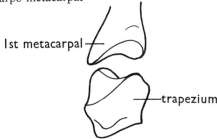

Saddle joint

Pivot joint

A peg rotates in a socket:

e.g. (i) the odontoid peg of the axis within the ring of the atlas allows turning of the head;

(ii) the head of the radius in the annular ligament at the superior radio-ulnar joint allows pronation and supination of the hand.

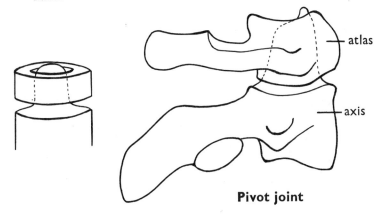

Pivot joint

Ball and socket joint

A rounded head fits in a cup-shaped cavity. Angular movements, circumduction and rotation can be performed freely—e.g. hip joint.

Ball and socket joint

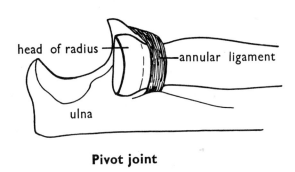

Pivot joint

THE PRINCIPAL JOINTS—*SUMMARY*

FIBROUS JOINTS OR SYNARTHROSES are found between:
1. Most of the **skull** bones—sutures formed by dovetailing.
2. **Teeth** and their sockets—gomphoses.
3. **Ribs** and **costal cartilages**.
4. Lower ends of **tibia** and **fibula**—syndesmosis—slight movement is possible.

CARTILAGINOUS JOINTS OR AMPHIARTHROSES are found between:
1. Bodies of the **free vertebrae** except atlas and axis—cartilages are intervertebral discs.
2. **Manubrium** and **gladiolus** } both these joints may become
3. **Gladiolus** and **xiphoid** } synarthroses later in life.
4. The two **pubes**, i.e. pubic symphysis } cartilage of this joint softens during pregnancy and allows greater movement at childbirth.

SYNOVIAL JOINTS OR DIARTHROSES are found between:
1. **Mandible** and **temporal** bones—condyloid.
2. **Occipital** condyles and **atlas**—condyloid.
3. **Atlas** and **axis**—pivot.
4. **Articular** processes of vertebrae—gliding.
5. **Vertebrae** and **ribs**—gliding.
6. **Costal cartilages** and **sternum**—gliding.
7. **Sternum** and **clavicle**—gliding with articular disc of cartilage.
8. **Clavicle** and **scapula**—gliding with slight rotation.
9. **Scapula** and **humerus**—ball and socket.
10. **Humerus** and **ulna**—hinge.
11. **Humerus** and **radius**—hinge, head of radius can also rotate.
12. Head of **radius** and **ulna**—pivot with annular ligament around the radius.
13. Lower ends of **radius** and **ulna**—pivot.
14. **Fore-arm** bones and **carpals**, i.e. wrist joint—condyloid.
15. **Carpals** and one another—gliding, results in various movements of the wrist as a whole.
16. **Trapezium** and **metacarpal** of thumb—saddle, allows apposition of the thumb.
17. **Carpals** and other **metacarpals**—gliding.
18. **Metacarpals** and one another—gliding.
19. **Metacarpals** and **phalanges**—condyloid.
20. **Phalanges** of each finger—hinge.
21. **Ilia and sacrum**—gliding but roughened surfaces prevent any actual movement, except at childbirth.
22. **Acetabulum** and head of **femur**—ball and socket.
23. **Femur** and **tibia**—structurally condyloid but functionally hinge with semilunar cartilages.
24. **Femur** and **patella**—gliding.
25. Head of **fibula** and **tibia**—gliding.
26. **Shin** bones and **talus**, i.e. ankle joint—hinge.
27. **Tarsals** and one another—gliding, summation of movements produces inversion and eversion of the foot.
28. **Tarsals** and **metatarsals**—gliding.
29. **Metatarsals** and one another—gliding.
30. **Metatarsals** and **phalanges**—condyloid.
31. **Phalanges** of toes—hinge.

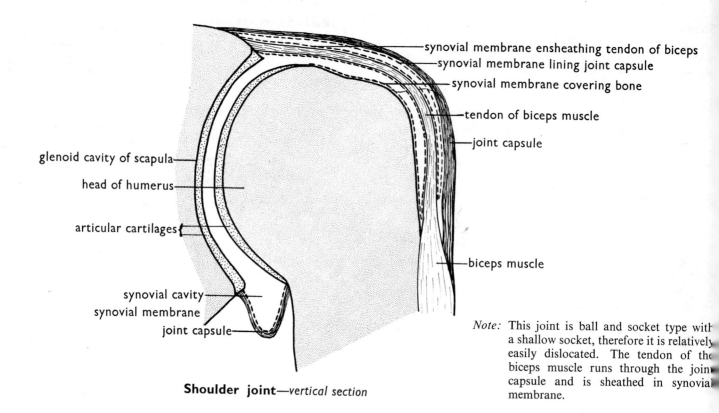

synovial membrane ensheathing tendon of biceps

synovial membrane lining joint capsule

synovial membrane covering bone

tendon of biceps muscle

joint capsule

glenoid cavity of scapula

head of humerus

articular cartilages

biceps muscle

synovial cavity

synovial membrane

joint capsule

Shoulder joint—*vertical section*

Note: This joint is ball and socket type with a shallow socket, therefore it is relatively easily dislocated. The tendon of the biceps muscle runs through the joint capsule and is sheathed in synovial membrane.

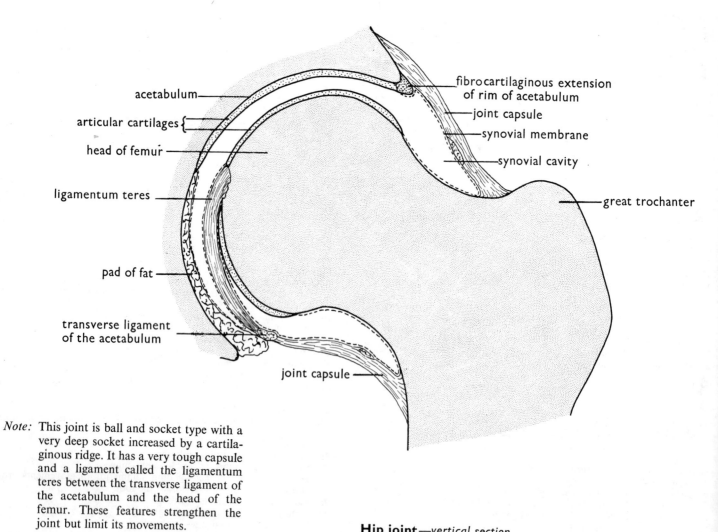

acetabulum

articular cartilages

head of femur

ligamentum teres

pad of fat

transverse ligament of the acetabulum

joint capsule

fibrocartilaginous extension of rim of acetabulum

joint capsule

synovial membrane

synovial cavity

great trochanter

Note: This joint is ball and socket type with a very deep socket increased by a cartilaginous ridge. It has a very tough capsule and a ligament called the ligamentum teres between the transverse ligament of the acetabulum and the head of the femur. These features strengthen the joint but limit its movements.

Hip joint—*vertical section*

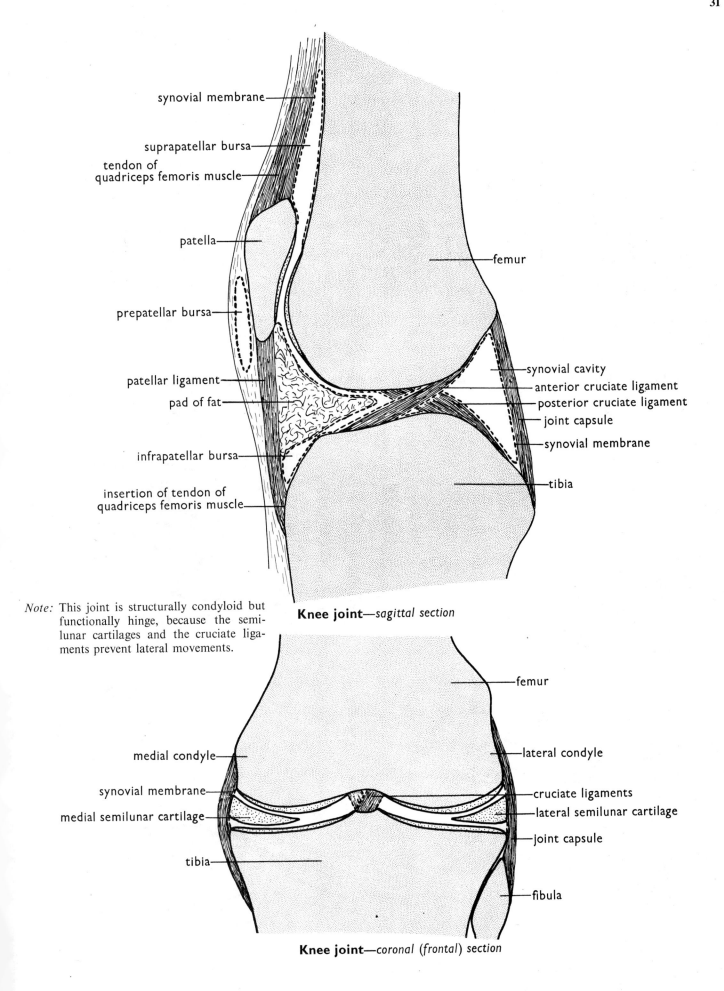

synovial membrane

suprapatellar bursa

tendon of
quadriceps femoris muscle

patella

prepatellar bursa

patellar ligament

pad of fat

infrapatellar bursa

insertion of tendon of
quadriceps femoris muscle

femur

synovial cavity
anterior cruciate ligament
posterior cruciate ligament
joint capsule
synovial membrane

tibia

Note: This joint is structurally condyloid but functionally hinge, because the semilunar cartilages and the cruciate ligaments prevent lateral movements.

Knee joint—*sagittal section*

femur

medial condyle

synovial membrane

medial semilunar cartilage

tibia

lateral condyle

cruciate ligaments

lateral semilunar cartilage

joint capsule

fibula

Knee joint—*coronal (frontal) section*

THE MUSCULAR SYSTEM

The muscular system is concerned with the production of movement both of the body as a whole and of the internal organs. Muscle tissue consists of cells which are capable of contraction. There are three types of muscle in the human body, each concerned with a different type of movement.

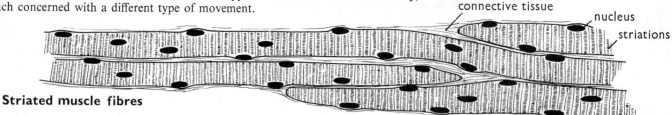

Striated muscle fibres

Note. There are numerous nuclei in each cell and fibrils in the cytoplasm show marked striations. There is connective tissue between the cells.

1. Skeletal Muscle

Skeletal muscle is attached to the skeleton either directly or indirectly, is controlled by the **voluntary** parts of the nervous system and is composed of large **striated** cells bound together into bundles or sheets by **areolar connective tissue**. Skeletal muscles, with the exception of sphincters, are attached to their origins and insertions by **white fibrous tissue** which may form rounded **tendons** or flattened **aponeuroses**. A **fascia** is a sheet of dense connective tissue around or over muscles. In some places the fasciae have enough white fibrous tissue to act as aponeuroses.

Each skeletal muscle fibre is served by a nerve fibre which ends in a **neuromuscular plate** through which the stimulus to contract is passed. Each fibre acts in an "all or nothing" manner, and the degree of contraction of the whole muscle is proportional to the number of fibres acting. Normally a few fibres are stimulated, maintaining **tone** even when the muscle is at rest. When many fibres are stimulated together, they produce shortening of the whole muscle or tension between the two ends. The end which usually remains fixed during contraction is the **origin**, and the end which moves is the **insertion**. If the stimulus is prolonged or too frequently repeated the muscle may become fatigued.

In many cases the bones act as levers. In such a lever the joint usually acts as the fulcrum, the skeletal muscle acts as the effort and the part supported or moved acts as the load.

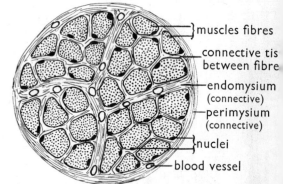

Skeletal muscle—*T.S.*

Note. The fibres are bound in bundles called fasciculi.

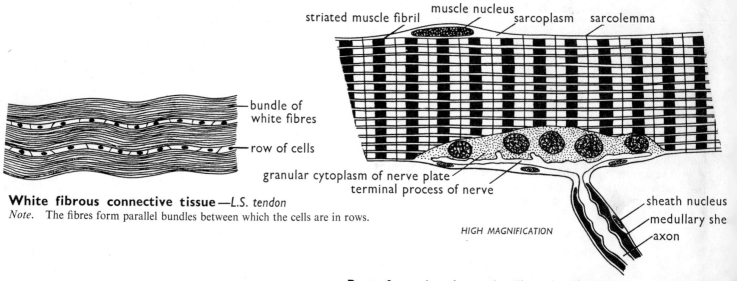

White fibrous connective tissue—*L.S. tendon*

Note. The fibres form parallel bundles between which the cells are in rows.

Part of a striated muscle fibre showing neuromuscular plat

HIGH MAGNIFICATION

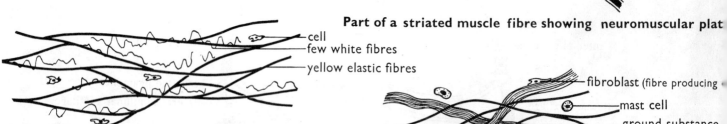

Yellow elastic connective tissue—*teased ligament*

Note. The yellow elastic fibres anastomose and there are cells scattered between them.

Areolar connective tissue

Note. The mixture of white and yellow elastic fibres and ground substance varies different parts where this tissue is found.

Visceral Muscle

[Vi]sceral muscle is associated with the viscera; it is controlled by the **involuntary** parts of the nervous system, and is composed of minute spindle-shaped [ce]lls whose fibrils are so fine that they appear **unstriated** in ordinary microscopic examination. The visceral muscle cells are bound together in sheets by [ar]eolar connective tissue which often contains much yellow elastic tissue. Each visceral muscle fibre is not served by a separate nerve but the sheet as a [wh]ole is served by a nerve plexus. Tone is present even when the main nervous connections are severed, and the contraction is smooth though slower than [th]at of skeletal muscle. Visceral muscle does not become fatigued. Visceral muscle fibres are found in the walls of the visceral organs and blood vessels, [an]d in the skin. They often form separate circular and longitudinal coats whose actions are mutually antagonistic.

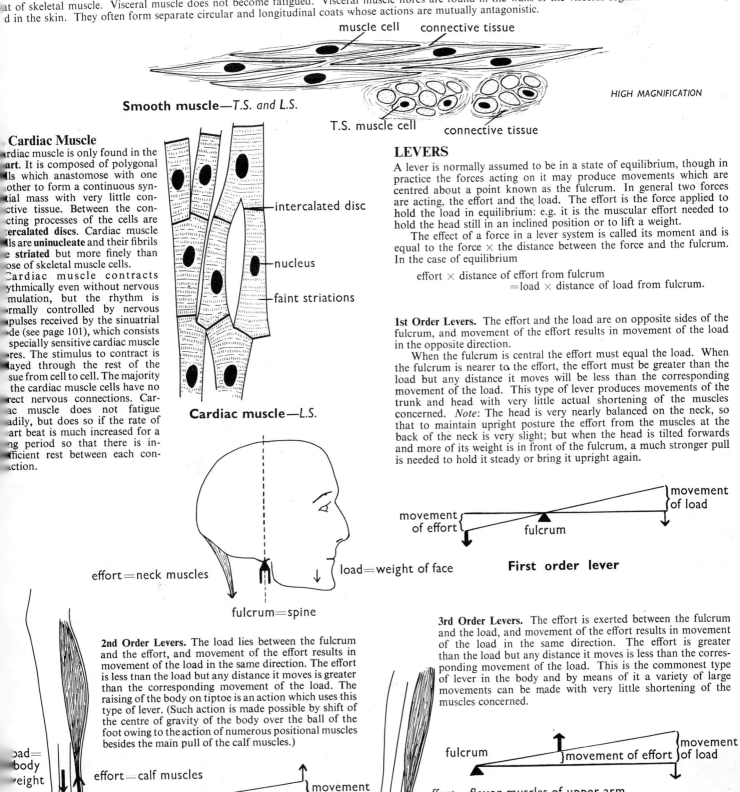

muscle cell   connective tissue

Smooth muscle—T.S. and L.S.

HIGH MAGNIFICATION

T.S. muscle cell   connective tissue

Cardiac Muscle

[C]ardiac muscle is only found in the [he]art. It is composed of polygonal [ce]lls which anastomose with one [an]other to form a continuous syn[ci]tial mass with very little con[ne]ctive tissue. Between the con[ne]cting processes of the cells are [in]tercalated discs. Cardiac muscle [ce]lls are **uninucleate** and their fibrils [ar]e **striated** but more finely than [th]ose of skeletal muscle cells. [C]ardiac muscle contracts [rh]ythmically even without nervous [sti]mulation, but the rhythm is [no]rmally controlled by nervous [im]pulses received by the sinuatrial [no]de (see page 101), which consists [of] specially sensitive cardiac muscle [fib]res. The stimulus to contract is [re]layed through the rest of the [tis]sue from cell to cell. The majority [of] the cardiac muscle cells have no [di]rect nervous connections. Car[di]ac muscle does not fatigue [re]adily, but does so if the rate of [he]art beat is much increased for a [lo]ng period so that there is in[su]fficient rest between each con[tra]ction.

—intercalated disc

—nucleus

—faint striations

Cardiac muscle—L.S.

LEVERS

A lever is normally assumed to be in a state of equilibrium, though in practice the forces acting on it may produce movements which are centred about a point known as the fulcrum. In general two forces are acting, the effort and the load. The effort is the force applied to hold the load in equilibrium: e.g. it is the muscular effort needed to hold the head still in an inclined position or to lift a weight.

The effect of a force in a lever system is called its moment and is equal to the force × the distance between the force and the fulcrum. In the case of equilibrium

effort × distance of effort from fulcrum
 =load × distance of load from fulcrum.

1st Order Levers. The effort and the load are on opposite sides of the fulcrum, and movement of the effort results in movement of the load in the opposite direction.

When the fulcrum is central the effort must equal the load. When the fulcrum is nearer to the effort, the effort must be greater than the load but any distance it moves will be less than the corresponding movement of the load. This type of lever produces movements of the trunk and head with very little actual shortening of the muscles concerned. *Note*: The head is very nearly balanced on the neck, so that to maintain upright posture the effort from the muscles at the back of the neck is very slight; but when the head is tilted forwards and more of its weight is in front of the fulcrum, a much stronger pull is needed to hold it steady or bring it upright again.

movement of load

movement of effort   fulcrum

First order lever

effort=neck muscles   load=weight of face

fulcrum=spine

2nd Order Levers. The load lies between the fulcrum and the effort, and movement of the effort results in movement of the load in the same direction. The effort is less than the load but any distance it moves is greater than the corresponding movement of the load. The raising of the body on tiptoe is an action which uses this type of lever. (Such action is made possible by shift of the centre of gravity of the body over the ball of the foot owing to the action of numerous positional muscles besides the main pull of the calf muscles.)

load= body weight

effort=calf muscles

movement of load   movement of effort

fulcrum

Second order lever

fulcrum=ball of foot

3rd Order Levers. The effort is exerted between the fulcrum and the load, and movement of the effort results in movement of the load in the same direction. The effort is greater than the load but any distance it moves is less than the corresponding movement of the load. This is the commonest type of lever in the body and by means of it a variety of large movements can be made with very little shortening of the muscles concerned.

fulcrum   movement of effort   movement of load

effort=flexor muscles of upper arm

load=hand and fore-arm

fulcrum=elbow joint

Third order lever

The chief muscles which move the head and trunk

Muscle	Origin	Insertion	Action of two sides together	Action of one side only	Notes
Sternomastoid	sternum and clavicle	mastoid process	flex neck	flexes neck laterally and rotates it	When the head is fixed this muscle raises sternum.
Splenius	lower half of ligamentum nuchae and 1st six thoracic vertibrae	mastoid process and occipital bone	extend neck	flexes neck laterally and rotates it	
Semispinalis capitis	4th cervical to 5th thoracic vertebrae	occipital bone	extend neck	rotates neck	
Sacro-spinalis (Erector spinae)	sacrum and iliac crest with additional fibres from ribs and lower vertebrae	ribs, vertebrae and mastoid process	extend trunk	flexes trunk laterally	This muscle divides into three columns, ilio-costo-cervicalis longissimus and spinalis.
Semispinalis cervicis and semispinalis thoracis	transverse processes of thoracic vertebrae	spinous processes of vertebrae 6 or 7 above	extend trunk and straighten thoracic curvature		These muscles are not shown in the diagrams because they lie under the sacrospinalis.
Multifidus	ilium, sacrum and transverse or articular processes of vertebrae	spinous processes of vertebrae one to four above	extend trunk and neck	flex trunk and neck laterally and rotate them	They are chiefly postural in function aiding rather than causing the larger movements.
Rotatores	transverse processes of thoracic vertebrae	laminae of thoracic vertebrae next above		rotate trunk	
Levatores costarum (12 pairs)	transverse processes of last cervical and all but last thoracic vertebrae	ribs next below	rotate heads of ribs	flex trunk laterally and rotate it	
Quadratus lumborum	iliac crest and ilio-lumbar ligament	12th rib and transverse processes of upper four lumbar vertebrae	extend trunk	flexes trunk laterally and steadies lowest rib	See also page 44.
Rectus abdominis	pubis	5th to 7th costal cartilages	flex trunk ventrally	flexes trunk laterally	See also page 49.
External oblique and internal oblique	For details see the abdominal wall (page 49)		flex trunk ventrally	flex trunk laterally and rotate it	
Psoas minor	12th thoracic and 1st lumbar vertebrae	pubis and iliac fascia	help to flex trunk ventrally		These muscles are weak and often missing. See fig., page 44
Psoas major	For details see hip muscles (page 42)		flex trunk ventrally	flexes trunk laterally and flexes hip	

The chief muscles which move the ribs (see also muscles of respiration, page 52)

Muscle	Origin	Insertion	Action	Notes
External intercostals (11 pairs)	lower borders of upper eleven pairs of ribs	further forward on upper border of rib next below in each case	help to raise the ribs	The chief function of these muscles is to maintain the shape of the wall of the thorax.
Internal intercostals (11 pairs)	inner surfaces of upper eleven pairs of ribs and the costal cartilages	further back on the upper border of the rib or costal cartilage next below	help to raise the ribs	
Scalenus muscles	transverse processes of cervical vertebrae	1st and 2nd ribs	raise upper ribs	Acting from below these muscles help to flex the neck.
Serratus posterior superior	lower part of the ligamentum nuchae and spines of first three thoracic vertebrae	2nd to 5th ribs	raises ribs	
Serratus posterior inferior	spines of 11th thoracic to 2nd or 3rd lumbar vertebrae	9th to 12th ribs	draws lower ribs downward and backwards	This muscle helps to steady the origin of the diaphragm.
Sternocostalis	sternum	costal cartilages	draws down costal cartilages	This muscle is inside the thoracic cage and is not shown in diagram.

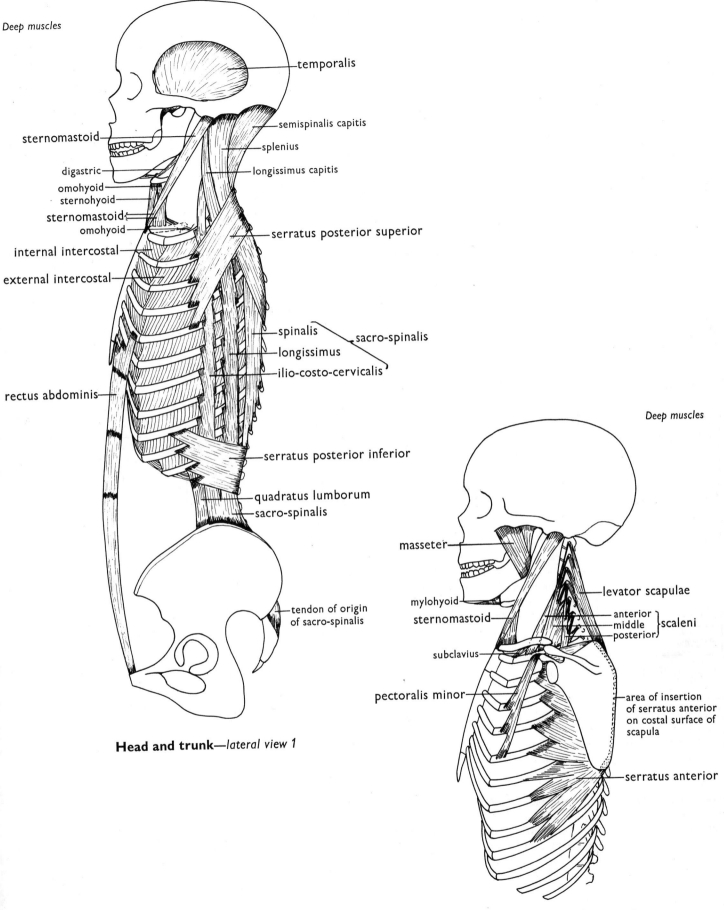

Deep muscles

temporalis

semispinalis capitis

sternomastoid

splenius

digastric

longissimus capitis

omohyoid

sternohyoid

sternomastoid

omohyoid

serratus posterior superior

internal intercostal

external intercostal

spinalis

longissimus

sacro-spinalis

rectus abdominis

ilio-costo-cervicalis

serratus posterior inferior

quadratus lumborum

sacro-spinalis

tendon of origin
of sacro-spinalis

Head and trunk—*lateral view 1*

Deep muscles

masseter

levator scapulae

mylohyoid

anterior

sternomastoid

middle

scaleni

posterior

subclavius

area of insertion
of serratus anterior
on costal surface of
scapula

pectoralis minor

serratus anterior

Head and trunk—*lateral view 2*

The muscles of mastication

Muscle	Origin	Insertion	Action	Notes
Masseter	zygomatic arch	mandible	raises lower jaw	
Temporalis	temporal fossa	coronoid process of mandible	raises and retracts lower jaw	
Medial pterygoid	pterygoid plate of sphenoid, palatine and maxilla	angle of mandible	raises lower jaw	These muscles are internal to t[he] temporalis muscle and coronoid pr[o]cess and are not shown in diagra[m]
Lateral pterygoid	pterygoid plate and great wing of sphenoid	neck of mandible	opens mouth and protrudes lower jaw	The right lateral pterygoid acting wi[th] the left elevators of the jaw and alte[r]nating with the left lateral pterygo[id] and right elevators produces chewin[g]

The chief muscles of facial expression

Muscle	Origin	Insertion	Action	Notes
Occipito-frontalis			moves scalp, raises eyebrows and wrinkles forehead	
(a) occipital part	occipital bone	epicranial aponeurosis		
(b) frontal part	epicranial aponeurosis	skin of eyebrow region		
Auricularis	epicranial aponeurosis and temporal bone	cartilage of the pinna	move pinna slightly	There are three of these small muscles vestiges of those which cock the ear of other mammals.
Orbicularis oculi	medial parts of rim of orbit	forms a sphincter round the eye and across the eyelid	closes lids	
Levator palpebrae	back of orbit	upper lid	opens upper lid	See fig., page 69.
Orbicularis oris	sphincter muscle round the mouth		closes mouth	
Buccinator	maxilla and mandible	angle of mouth	compresses cheeks	
Risorius	parotid fascia	angle of mouth	retracts angle of mouth	
Elevators of corners of mouth	maxillae	angles of mouth	produce cheerful expression	
Depressors of corners of mouth	mandible	angles of mouth	produce dismal expression	
Elevators of upper lip	maxillae and zygomatic bones	upper lip	open mouth	
Depressors of lower lip	mandible	lower lip	open mouth	
Platysma	fascia over pectoralis major and deltoid muscles	mandible and skin and muscles of lower part of face	helps to draw down mandible and lower lip and wrinkles skin of neck	Used during yawning.
Nasal muscles	maxillae	nose	compress and dilate the nasal openings	

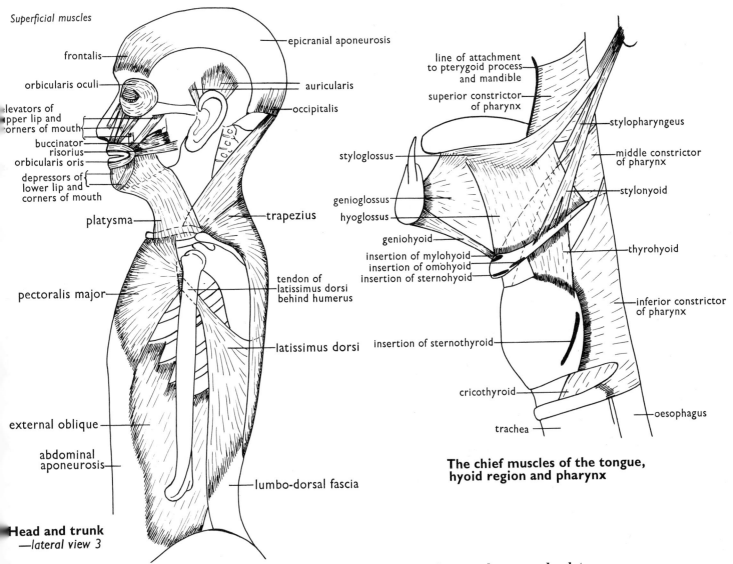

Superficial muscles

frontalis

epicranial aponeurosis

orbicularis oculi

auricularis

occipitalis

levators of upper lip and corners of mouth

buccinator

risorius

orbicularis oris

depressors of lower lip and corners of mouth

platysma

trapezius

pectoralis major

tendon of latissimus dorsi behind humerus

latissimus dorsi

external oblique

abdominal aponeurosis

lumbo-dorsal fascia

Head and trunk
—*lateral view 3*

line of attachment to pterygoid process and mandible

superior constrictor of pharynx

stylopharyngeus

styloglossus

middle constrictor of pharynx

genioglossus

stylonyoid

hyoglossus

geniohyoid

insertion of mylohyoid

insertion of omohyoid

insertion of sternohyoid

thyrohyoid

inferior constrictor of pharynx

insertion of sternothyroid

cricothyroid

oesophagus

trachea

The chief muscles of the tongue, hyoid region and pharynx

The chief muscles which move the tongue, hyoid bone, larynx, pharynx and palate

Muscle	Origin	Insertion	Action	Notes
Genioglossus	mandible	tongue	pulls tongue forwards	These are the extrinsic muscles which move the tongue as a whole.
Hyoglossus	hyoid bone	tongue	depresses tongue	
Styloglossus	styloid process of temporal bone	tongue	pulls tongue upwards and backwards	
Longitudinal tongue muscles	lie completely inside the tongue		shorten tongue and curve it up or down	These are the intrinsic muscles of the tongue which change its shape.
Transverse tongue muscles	lie completely inside the tongue		make the tongue long and narrow	
Vertical tongue muscles	lie completely inside the tongue		make the tongue flat and round	
Mylohyoid	mandible	hyoid bone and muscle of opposite side	supports tongue and raises hyoid	These muscles form the floor of the mouth under the tongue.
Geniohyoid	mandible	hyoid bone	raises hyoid	These muscles move and steady the hyoid bone during movements of the tongue and swallowing.
Digastric	mandible and temporal bone	tendon between two halves of muscle connected to hyoid bone by a loop	raises hyoid	
Stylohyoid	styloid process	hyoid bone	raises hyoid	
Omohyoid	scapula	hyoid bone with connection to clavicle	depresses hyoid	
Sternohyoid	sternum and clavicle	hyoid bone	depresses hyoid	

The chief muscles which move the tongue, hyoid bone, larynx, pharynx and palate—*continued*

Muscle	Origin	Insertion	Action	Notes
Sternothyroid	sternum and 1st rib	thyroid cartilage	depresses larynx	
Thyrohyoid	thyroid cartilage	hyoid bone	depresses hyoid and raises larynx	These muscles are used during swallowing and ensure that food goes the right way and does not enter the larynx or naso pharynx. The palatopharyngeus and levator palati muscles are not visible in the diagrams.
Stylopharyngeus	styloid process	thyroid cartilage and wall of pharynx	raises larynx	
Palatopharyngeus	palate	thyroid cartilage and wall of pharynx	raises larynx	
Levator palati	temporal bone	palate	raises soft palate	
Constrictors of pharynx	pterygoid process, mandible, hyoid bone, thyroid and cricoid cartilages	the corresponding muscles of the other side	constrict pharynx	

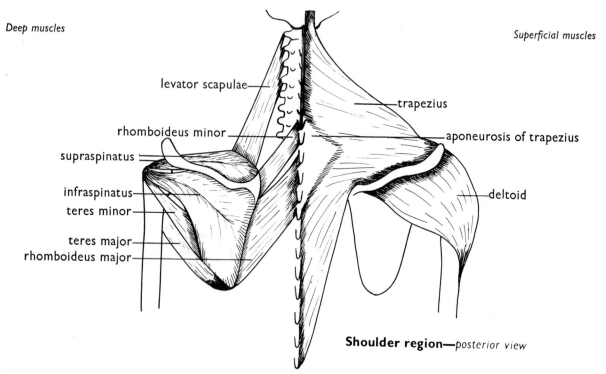

Deep muscles Superficial muscles

levator scapulae — trapezius — aponeurosis of trapezius — rhomboideus minor — supraspinatus — infraspinatus — teres minor — deltoid — teres major — rhomboideus major

Shoulder region—*posterior view*

The chief muscles which move the shoulder

Muscle	Origin	Insertion	Action	Notes
Sternomastoid	See trunk muscles— page 34			
Subclavius	1st rib	clavicle	draws shoulder downwards and forwards	All the muscles which move the shoulder are also used in combination with one another to steady the shoulder when the arm is moved and to adjust the angle of the glenoid cavity so that there is great freedom of movement.
Pectoralis minor	3rd–5th ribs	coracoid process of scapula	draws shoulder downwards and forwards	
Serratus anterior	upper eight or nine ribs	costal surface of vertebral border of scapula	draws shoulder forwards and rotates scapula	
Levator scapulae	upper four cervical vertebrae	upper part of vertebral border of scapula	elevates shoulder and rotates scapula	
Rhomboideus minor	ligamentum nuchae and 1st thoracic vertebrae	vertebral border of scapula	braces shoulder and rotates scapula	
Rhomboideus major	2nd–5th thoracic vertebrae	vertebral border of scapula	braces shoulder and rotates scapula	
Trapezius	occipital bone, ligamentum nuchae and all thoracic vertebrae	clavicle and spine of scapula	elevates and braces shoulder and rotates scapula	When the scapula is fixed this muscle pulls the head back.

The chief muscles which move the whole arm

Muscle	Origin	Insertion	Action	Notes
Coraco-brachialis	coracoid process of scapula	shaft of humerus	draws arm forwards and medially	When arm is raised it prevents side slip.
Pectoralis major	clavicle, sternum, cartilages of true ribs and abdominal aponeurosis	lateral lip of bicipital groove of humerus	draws arm forwards and medially, adducts and rotates it inwards	These two muscles also cause depression of the shoulder against force and elevation of the body on the arms, e.g. when climbing.
Latissimus dorsi	lower six thoracic vertebrae and through lumbo-dorsal fascia from lumbar vertebrae and iliac crest	bicipital groove of humerus	draws arm backwards, adducts and rotates it inwards	
Teres major	inferior angle of scapula	medial lip of bicipital groove of humerus	draws arm backwards and medially, adducts and rotates it inwards	
Subscapularis	subscapular fossa of scapula	lesser tuberosity of humerus	rotates arm inwards	These three muscles counteract slip of the head of the humerus when the deltoid is acting.
Teres minor	axillary border of scapula	greater tuberosity of humerus	rotates arm outwards	
Infraspinatus	infraspinous fossa of scapula	greater tuberosity of humerus	rotates arm outwards	
Supraspinatus	supraspinous fossa of scapula	greater tuberosity of humerus	abducts arm	Acting with the three muscles above it helps to steady the head of the humerus.
Deltoid	clavicle, acromion process and spine of scapula	deltoid tuberosity of humerus	(a) front draws arm forwards (b) back draws arm backwards (c) middle part abducts arm	Action (c) requires simultaneous rotation of the scapula.

The chief muscles which move the forearm, hand and fingers

Note. When the arm is in a relaxed position hanging by the side of the body, the palm of the hand faces medially, i.e. it is half way between the prone and the supine positions. In this position the flexors of the hand and wrist are medial and the extensors are lateral, while the flexors of the elbow are anterior and the extensors are posterior. (Most books show the forearm twisted into the supine position with the flexors of the hand and wrist and the brachioradialis anterior, and with the ulnar flexor and the extensors posterior.)

Muscle	Origin	Insertion	Action	Notes
Triceps (a) long head (b) medial head (c) lateral head	scapula humerus humerus	by strong tendon on olecranon process of ulna	extends elbow	This is the only muscle at the back of the upper arm.
Anconeus	lateral epicondyle of humerus	lateral part of olecranon process of ulna	extends elbow	
Brachialis	shaft of humerus	coronoid process and tuberosity of ulna	flexes elbow	The main part of this muscle crosses the elbow.
Brachioradialis	lateral supracondylar ridge of humerus	distal part of radius	flexes elbow	The main part of this muscle lies below the elbow.
Biceps (brachii) (a) long head (b) short head	scapula (passes through shoulder joint capsule) coracoid process of scapula	by a strong tendon on tuberosity of radius	flexes elbow and supinates fore-arm and hand	This is the main muscle of the front of the upper arm. Because it originates from the scapula it helps to flex and steady the shoulder joint.
Supinator	lateral epicondyle of humerus	lateral surface of radius	supinates fore-arm and hand	
Pronator teres	above medial epicondyle of humerus and coronoid process of ulna	middle of shaft of radius	pronates fore-arm and hand	
Pronator quadratus	distal part of ulna	distal part of shaft of radius	keeps radius and ulna together	The pronating action of this muscle is very weak.
Superficial extensors of wrist and fingers	lateral epicondyle of humerus	metacarpals and phalanges	extend wrist and fingers	The radial flexor and extensor of the wrist when acting together abduct the hand while the ulnar flexor and extensor of the wrist adduct the hand. The tendons of all these muscles are held in place at the wrist by fibrous bands called the extensor retinaculum and the flexor retinaculum respectively.
Deep extensors of fingers	ulna and radius	phalanges of thumb and forefinger	extend thumb and forefinger	
Superficial flexors of wrist and fingers	medial epicondyle of humerus	metacarpals, palmar aponeurosis and phalanges	flex wrist and fingers	
Deep flexors of fingers	ulna and radius	phalanges	flex thumb and fingers	

Note. In the palm of the hand there are additional small muscles causing flexion, abduction and adduction of the fingers and apposition of the thumb and little finger.

40

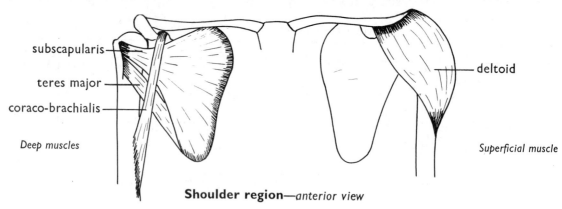

subscapularis

teres major

coraco-brachialis

deltoid

Deep muscles

Superficial muscle

Shoulder region—*anterior view*

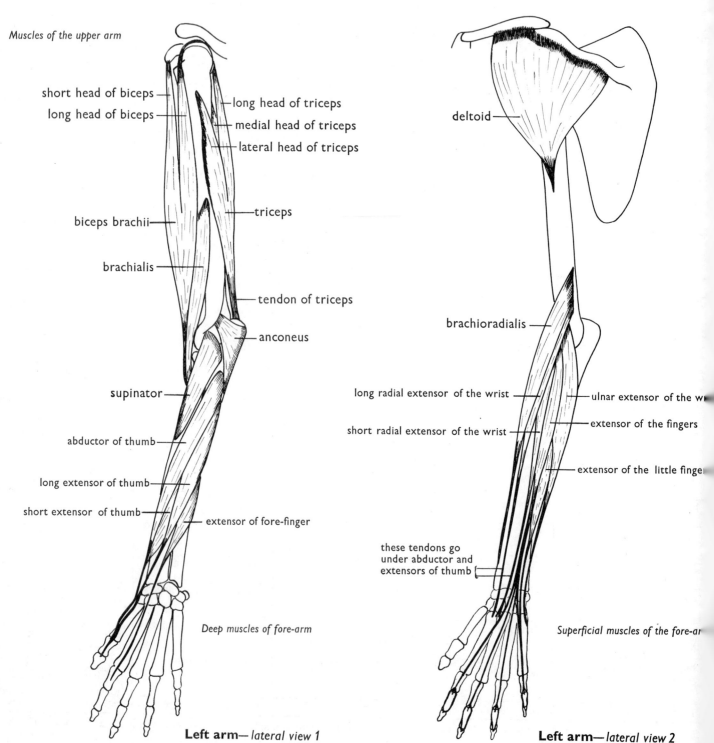

Muscles of the upper arm

short head of biceps

long head of biceps

long head of triceps

medial head of triceps

lateral head of triceps

biceps brachii

triceps

brachialis

tendon of triceps

anconeus

supinator

abductor of thumb

long extensor of thumb

short extensor of thumb

extensor of fore-finger

Deep muscles of fore-arm

deltoid

brachioradialis

long radial extensor of the wrist

ulnar extensor of the w

short radial extensor of the wrist

extensor of the fingers

extensor of the little finge

these tendons go
under abductor and
extensors of thumb

Superficial muscles of the fore-a

Left arm—*lateral view 1*

Left arm—*lateral view 2*

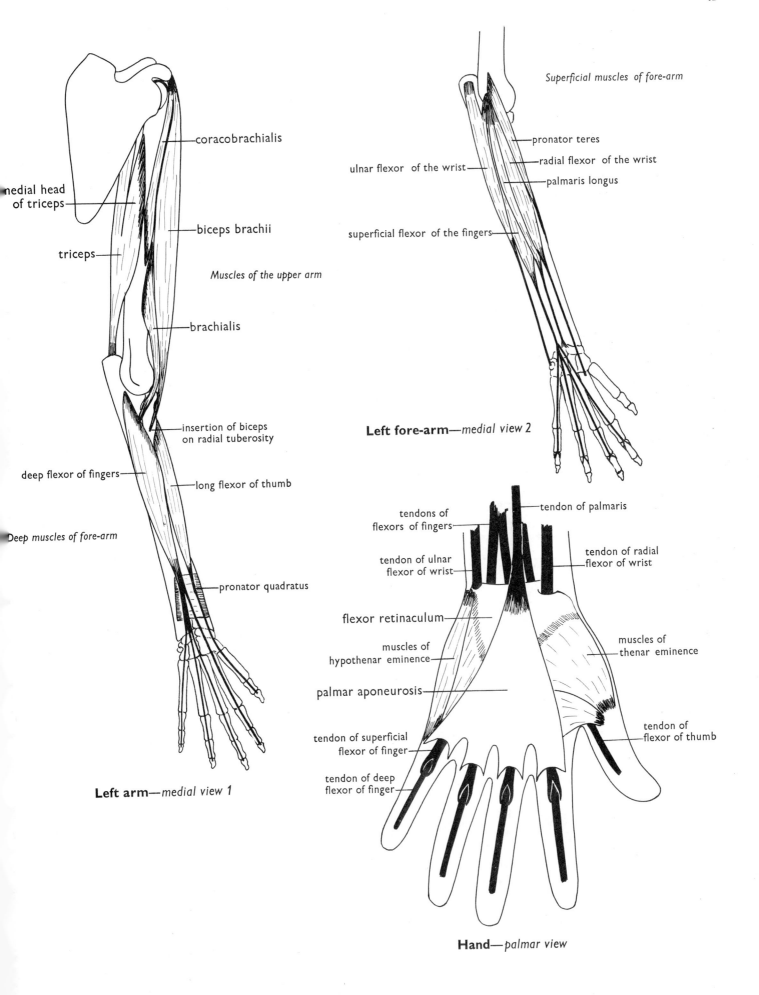

coracobrachialis

medial head of triceps

biceps brachii

triceps

Muscles of the upper arm

brachialis

insertion of biceps on radial tuberosity

deep flexor of fingers

long flexor of thumb

Deep muscles of fore-arm

pronator quadratus

Left arm—*medial view 1*

Superficial muscles of fore-arm

pronator teres

ulnar flexor of the wrist

radial flexor of the wrist

palmaris longus

superficial flexor of the fingers

Left fore-arm—*medial view 2*

tendon of palmaris

tendons of flexors of fingers

tendon of ulnar flexor of wrist

tendon of radial flexor of wrist

flexor retinaculum

muscles of hypothenar eminence

muscles of thenar eminence

palmar aponeurosis

tendon of superficial flexor of finger

tendon of flexor of thumb

tendon of deep flexor of finger

Hand—*palmar view*

The chief muscles which move the lower limb

Note. There is so much overlap of function with muscles acting on hip and knee, and on knee and ankle, that it is impossible to separate the different groups distinctly. Also, because the knee bends in the opposite direction from the hip and ankle some muscles may be both flexors and extensors.

Muscle	Origin	Insertion	Action	Notes
Piriformis	front of sacrum	greater trochanter of femur	rotates femur laterally	This group of short muscles limits the medial rotation inevitable with the action of the large flexor muscles and resists strain on the hip joint so that the capsular ligaments can be thin enough not to restrict movement.
Obturator internus	inner surface of pelvis	greater trochanter of femur	rotates femur laterally	
Gemellus superior and inferior	spine and tuberosity of ischium	tendon of obturator internus	rotate femur laterally	
Quadratus femoris	tuberosity of ischium	trochanteric crest of femur	rotates femur laterally	
Obturator externus	outer surface of pubis, ischium and obturator membrane	trochanteric fossa of femur	rotates femur laterally	The actual movements produced by these muscles are very slight.
Pectineus	pubis	near lesser trochanter of femur	adducts femur and flexes hip	
Adductors	pubis and ischium	linea aspera and supra-condylar line	adduct and rotate femur laterally	These muscles can also draw the abducted leg medially.
Ilio-psoas (a) psoas major	12th thoracic and all lumbar vertebrae	lesser trochanter of femur	rotate femur medially and flex hip	
(b) iliacus	iliac fossa and front of sacrum			
Tensor fasciae latae	outer part of iliac crest	fascia lata	keeps the fascial sheath of the thigh tensed and therefore helps to abduct and rotate femur medially and to extend knee	
Gluteus maximus	posterior gluteal line of ilium and crest above and also sacrum and coccyx	fascia lata and gluteal tuberosity of femur	tenses fascia lata and extends hip, therefore raises trunk after stooping	These muscles are very important in maintaining the upright posture of the trunk on the legs, standing, walking, etc.
Gluteus medius	between posterior and middle gluteal lines of ilium	greater trochanter of femur	abducts femur and anterior fibres rotate it medially	
Gluteus minimus	between middle and inferior gluteal lines of ilium	greater trochanter of femur	abducts femur and anterior fibres rotate it medially	
Gracilis	pubis and ischium	below medial condyle of tibia	adducts and rotates femur medially, flexes knee	
Semitendinosus	tuberosity of ischium	below medial condyle of tibia	extend hip and flex knee and when knee semi-flexed rotate femur medially	These muscles are collectively known as the "hamstrings".
Semimembranosus	tuberosity of ischium	medial condyle of tibia		
Biceps femoris (a) long head (b) short head	tuberosity of ischium / linea aspera	head of fibula and lateral condyle of tibia	extends hip and flexes knee and when knee semi-flexed rotates femur laterally	
Sartorius	anterior superior iliac spine	below medial condyle of tibia	flexes hip and knee, abducts and rotates femur laterally	
Quadriceps femoris (a) rectus femoris	above acetabulum	through the patella and patellar ligament on to tubercle of tibia	together extend knee and the rectus femoris part helps to flex hip	The tendon of this muscle forms a large part of the capsule of the knee joint.
(b) vastus lateralis	greater trochanter and linea aspera			
(c) vastus intermedius	shaft of femur			
(d) vastus medialis	trochanteric and spiral lines and linea aspera			

CONTINUED ON PAGE 47

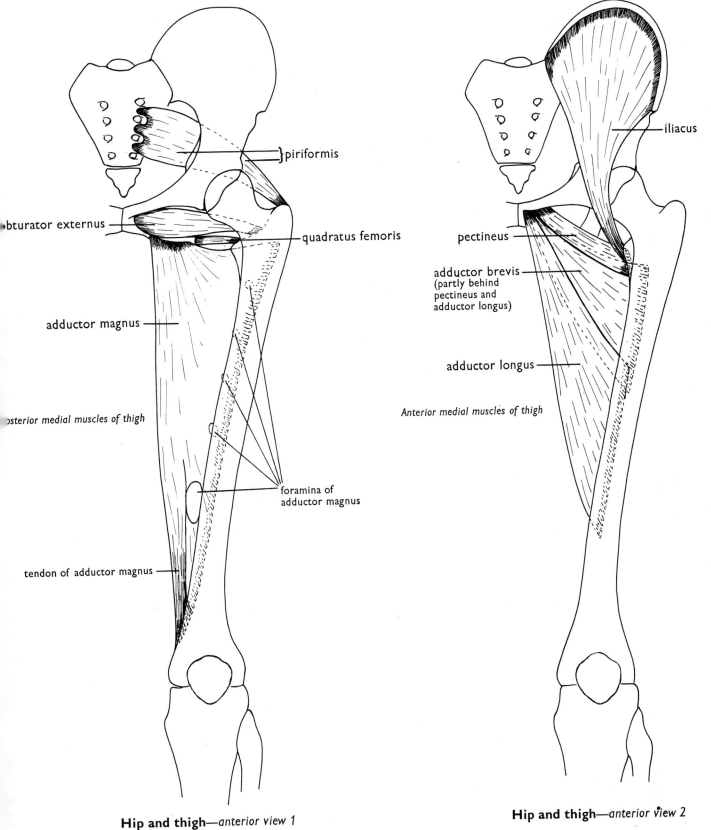

}piriformis

obturator externus

quadratus femoris

adductor magnus

posterior medial muscles of thigh

foramina of
adductor magnus

tendon of adductor magnus

Hip and thigh—*anterior view 1*

iliacus

pectineus

adductor brevis
(partly behind
pectineus and
adductor longus)

adductor longus

Anterior medial muscles of thigh

Hip and thigh—*anterior view 2*

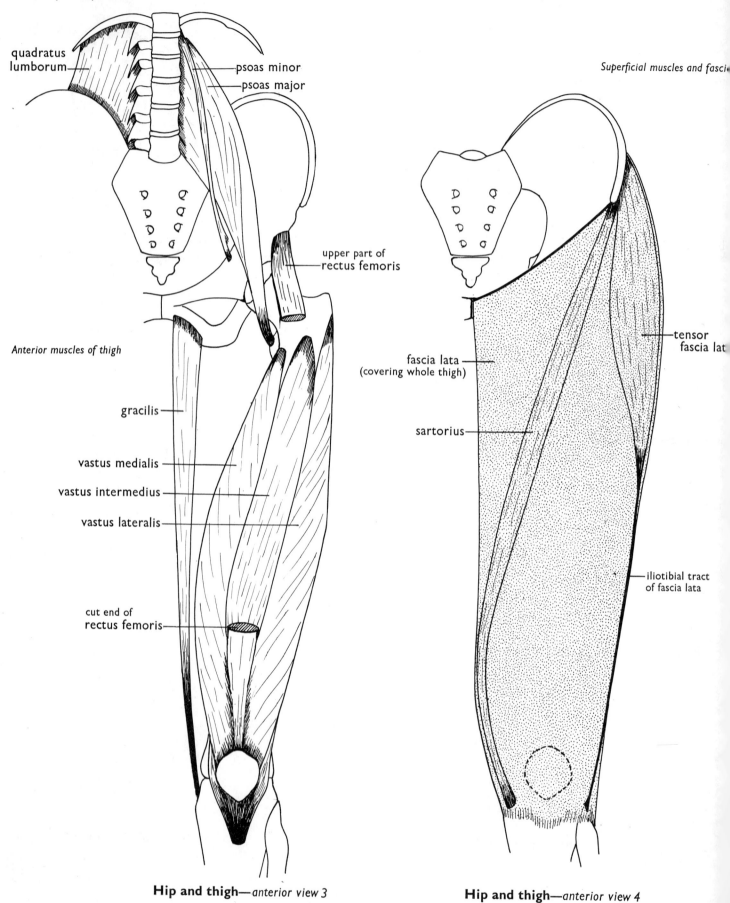

Muscles of back of abdomen

quadratus
lumborum

psoas minor

psoas major

upper part of
rectus femoris

Anterior muscles of thigh

fascia lata
(covering whole thigh)

tensor
fascia lat

gracilis

sartorius

vastus medialis

vastus intermedius

vastus lateralis

iliotibial tract
of fascia lata

cut end of
rectus femoris

Hip and thigh—*anterior view 3*

Hip and thigh—*anterior view 4*

Deep posterior muscles of thigh

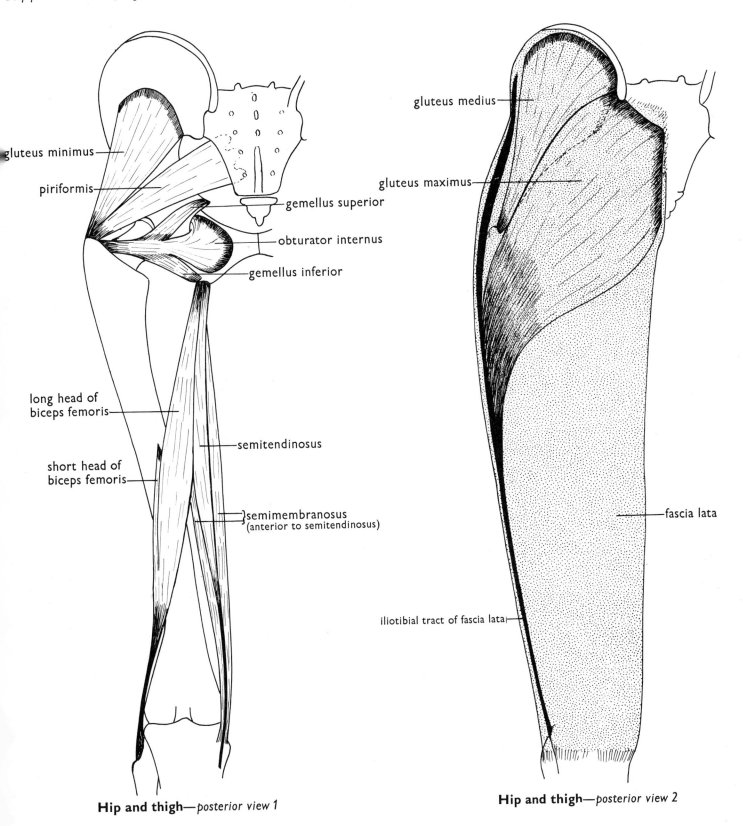

gluteus minimus

piriformis

gemellus superior

obturator internus

gemellus inferior

long head of
biceps femoris

semitendinosus

short head of
biceps femoris

}semimembranosus
(anterior to semitendinosus)

gluteus medius

gluteus maximus

fascia lata

iliotibial tract of fascia lata

Hip and thigh—*posterior view 1*

Hip and thigh—*posterior view 2*

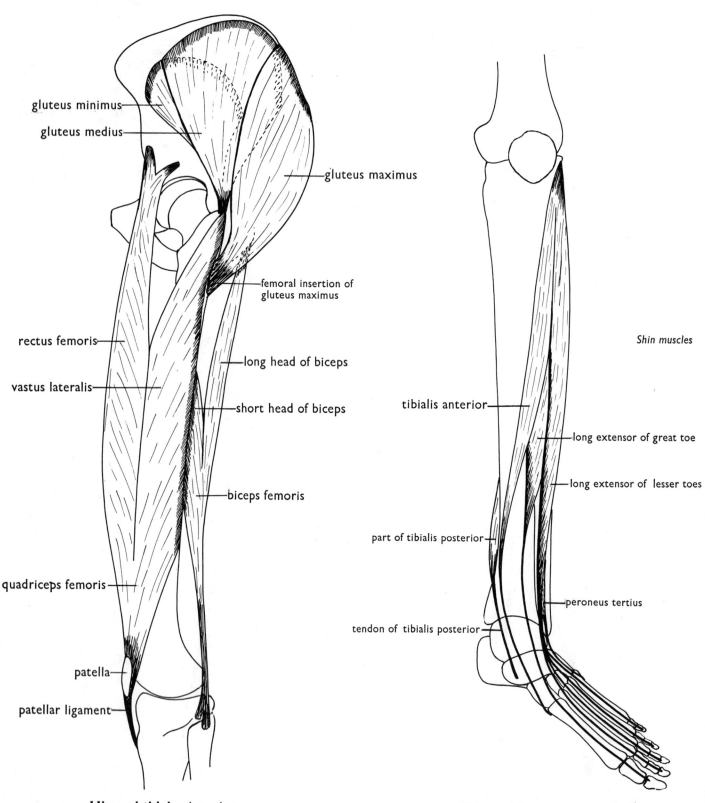

gluteus minimus

gluteus medius

gluteus maximus

femoral insertion of
gluteus maximus

rectus femoris

long head of biceps

vastus lateralis

short head of biceps

biceps femoris

quadriceps femoris

patella

patellar ligament

Hip and thigh—*lateral view*

Shin muscles

tibialis anterior

long extensor of great toe

long extensor of lesser toes

part of tibialis posterior

peroneus tertius

tendon of tibialis posterior

Shin and foot—*antero-medial view*

Deep muscles of calf

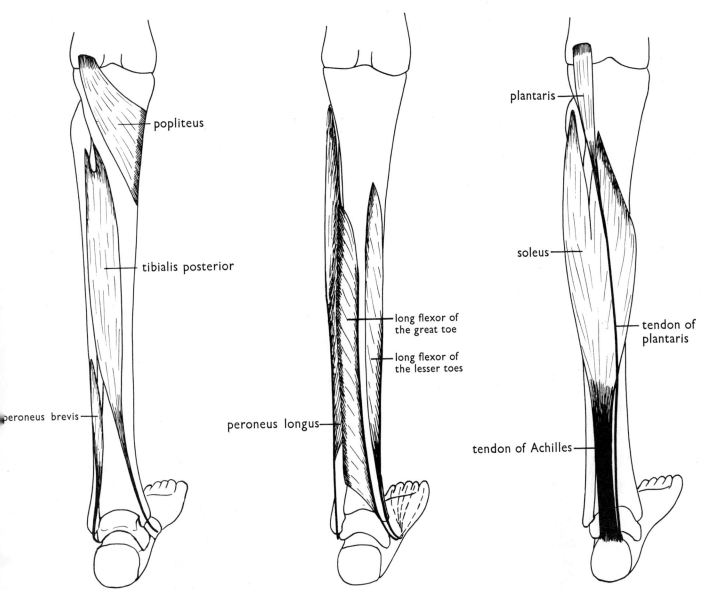

popliteus

tibialis posterior

peroneus brevis

Lower half of leg—*posterior view 1*

long flexor of the great toe

long flexor of the lesser toes

peroneus longus

Lower half of leg—*posterior view 2*

plantaris

soleus

tendon of plantaris

tendon of Achilles

Lower half of leg—*posterior view 3*

The chief muscles which move the lower limb—*continued from page 42*

Muscle	*Origin*	*Insertion*	*Action*	*Notes*
Popliteus	lateral condyle of femur	shaft of tibia	flexes knee and rotates tibia medially	
Gastrocnemius	lateral and medial condyles of femur	through tendon of Achilles on **calcaneum**	flexes knee and plantar-flexes ankle	These muscles give the force when walking, running, etc. Plantarflexion is equivalent to extension of other joints. It causes pointing of the foot and raising of the body on the toes.
Plantaris	above lateral condyle of femur	long tendon joins tendon of Achilles	accessory to gastrocnemius	
Soleus	fibula and tibia	through tendon of Achilles on calcaneum	plantarflexes ankle	

The chief muscles which move the lower limb—*continued*

Muscle	Origin	Insertion	Action	Notes
Tibialis posterior	tibia and fibula	navicular	inverts foot	
Tibialis anterior	lateral condyle and shaft of tibia, interosseus membrane	medial cuneiform and 1st metatarsal	inverts foot and rotates it laterally, dorsiflexes ankle	These muscles help balance when standing.
Peroneus (three muscles)	fibula	5th metatarsal and across sole of foot to 1st metatarsal	evert foot and rotate it medially, dorsiflex ankle	Their tendons are held in place at the ankle by fibrous bands, the superior and inferior extensor retinacula and the flexor retinaculum.
Long extensors of toes	fibula and lateral condyle of tibia	distal phalanges of toes	extend toes and dorsiflex ankle	
Long flexors of toes	back of tibia and fibula	distal phalanges of toes	flex toes and help to plantarflex ankle	

Note. There are also short extensors and flexors, adductors and abductors of the toes in the foot.

Superficial muscles of the calf

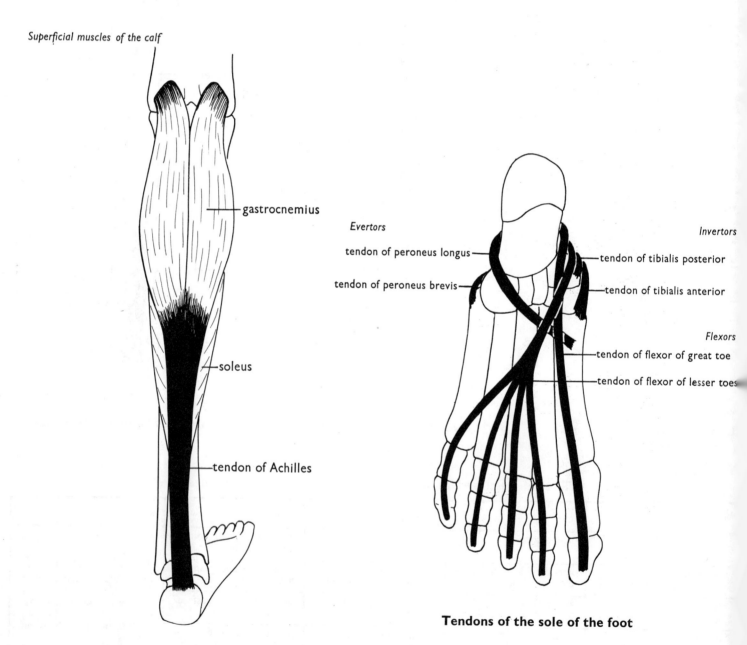

Lower half of leg—*posterior view 4*

Tendons of the sole of the foot

The muscles of the abdominal wall

(a) Posterior group
The back of the abdomen is supported by vertebrae but the quadratus lumborum and psoas muscles contribute to its wall—see page 34.

(b) Lateral and anterior group
The sides and front of the abdomen are formed of a continuous sheet of muscle and aponeurosis the main parts of which have three distinct layers.

Muscle	Origin	Insertion	Action	Notes
Transversus	inguinal ligament, iliac crest, lumbar fascia and cartilages of lower six ribs	conjoint tendon and linea alba through abdominal aponeurosis	supports the viscera, helps in vomiting, micturition, defaecation, parturition and forced expiration	The lumbar fascia lies around the muscles of the back in the lumbar region.
Internal oblique	inguinal ligament, iliac crest and lumbar fascia	conjoint tendon, linea alba through abdominal aponeurosis and lower three ribs	internal oblique of one side with external oblique of the other produce rotation, together they flex the trunk ventrally—ref. page 34	
External oblique	lower eight ribs	iliac crest and linea alba through abdominal aponeurosis		
Rectus abdominis	pubis	5th, 6th and 7th costal cartilages	supports viscera, helps vomiting, etc., and flexes trunk ventrally	The upper $\frac{2}{3}$ of this muscle lie in the aponeurotic sheath but the lower $\frac{1}{3}$ lies internal to the whole aponeurosis.
Pyramidalis	pubic symphysis	linea alba	tenses linea alba	

(c) Inferior group
The pelvic basin is lined with muscles many of which are concerned with movements of the thigh—see page 44,, but in addition there is a muscular sheet which supports the pelvic viscera. The anus and urethra have sphincters of voluntary muscle which control defaecation and micturition respectively.

Muscle	Origin	Insertion	Action	Notes
Levator ani	spine of ischium and tendinous arch of obturator fascia	coccyx, perineal body and fibres of muscle of opposite side	constricts rectum and vagina	These muscles form the pelvic floor.
Coccygeus	spine of ischium	sacrum and coccyx	pulls coccyx forwards after defaecation	

(d) Superior group
The upper wall of the abdomen is formed by the diaphragm, see page 52

The abdominal aponeurosis

The abdominal aponeurosis is a flattened sheet of tendinous fibres. Laterally it is in three layers attached to the external oblique, the internal oblique and the transversus muscles respectively, but medially the fibres from the two sides are interwoven to form a strong tendinous band called the **linea alba** which extends from the xiphoid process to the pubic symphysis.

The lower edge of the external layer of the aponeurosis is thickened to form the **inguinal ligament** which extends from the anterior superior iliac spine to the pubic tubercle. The middle layer of the aponeurosis is split above the **arcuate line**, i.e. for the upper three-quarters of its length, to form a sheath around the rectus abdominis muscle. The external part of this layer merges with the external layer of the aponeurosis and the internal part merges with the internal layer, the lower edge of which forms the **conjoint tendon** inserted on the pubic crest. The inguinal and conjoint tendons support the abdominal wall where there is greatest weakness, i.e. where it is perforated by the inguinal canals.

Each **inguinal canal** is about 40 mm long and lies parallel to and slightly above corresponding inguinal ligament. The inner end of the canal opens into the abdominal cavity at a **deep inguinal ring**, a perforation in the transversalis fascia half-way between the anterior superior iliac spine and the pubic symphysis. The outer end of each canal opens at a **superficial inguinal ring** which perforates the aponeurosis just above and lateral to the crest of the pubis. The conjoint tendon lies deep to this ring.

In the male the inguinal canals are wide because they transmit the spermatic cords but in the female they are narrow, because they transmit only the round ligaments of the uterus. As a result of this there is greater weakness in the regions of the inguinal rings of the male than of the female and inguinal hernia is much more common in men than in women. A further position of weakness is the umbilicus where the linea alba is perforated by the umbilical blood-vessels during foetal life. Though the perforation normally closes soon after birth umbilical hernia occasionally occurs, especially in infants.

Inner layer of muscle and aponeurosis

linea alba

abdominal aponeurosis

arcuate line

conjoint tendon (below superficial inguinal ring)

transversus

lumbar fascia

passage for rectus abdominis

position of deep inguinal ring

inguinal ligament

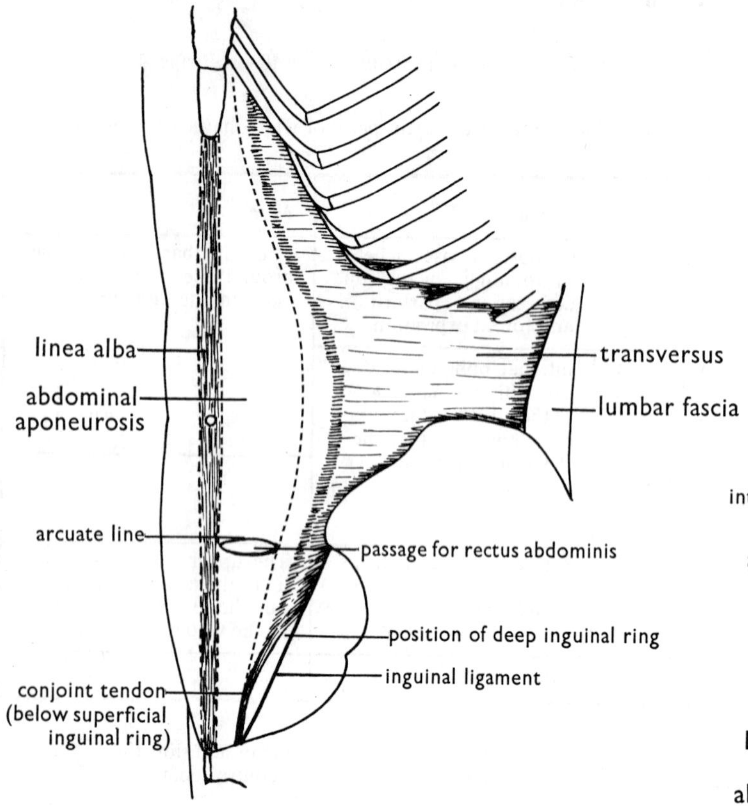

Abdominal wall—1

Middle layer of muscle and aponeurosis

tendinous intersections

rectus abdominis

linea alba

abdominal aponeurosis

conjoint tendon

internal oblique

lumbar fascia

inguinal line

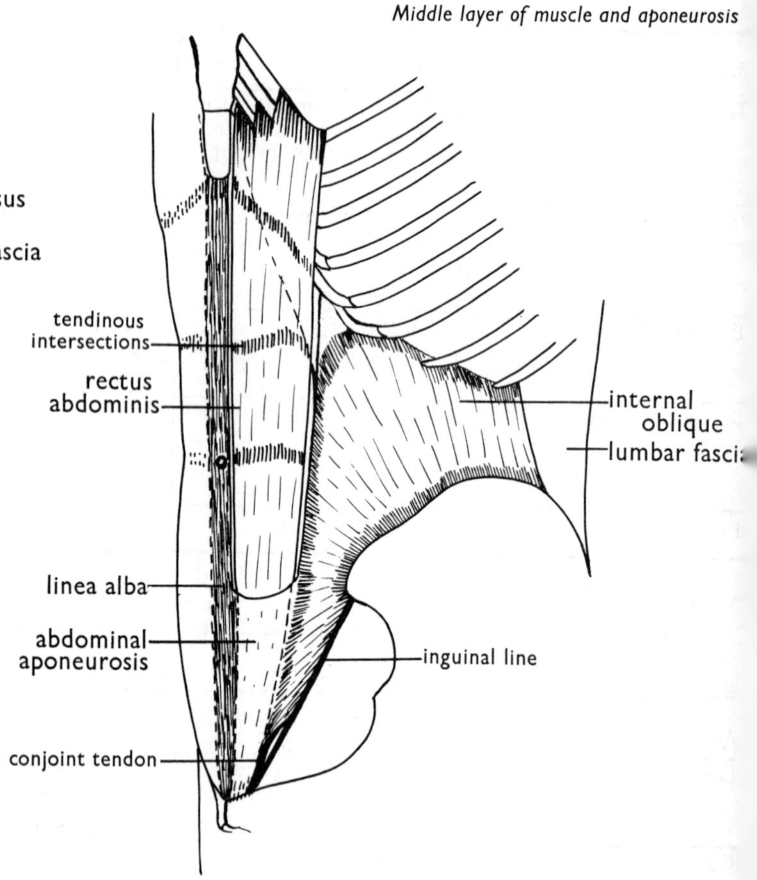

Abdominal wall—2

Outer layer of muscle and aponeurosis

linea alba

abdominal aponeurosis

pyramidalis

pectoralis major

external oblique

Abdominal wall—3

tendinous arch

urethral sphincter

coccygeus

levator ani

anal sphincter

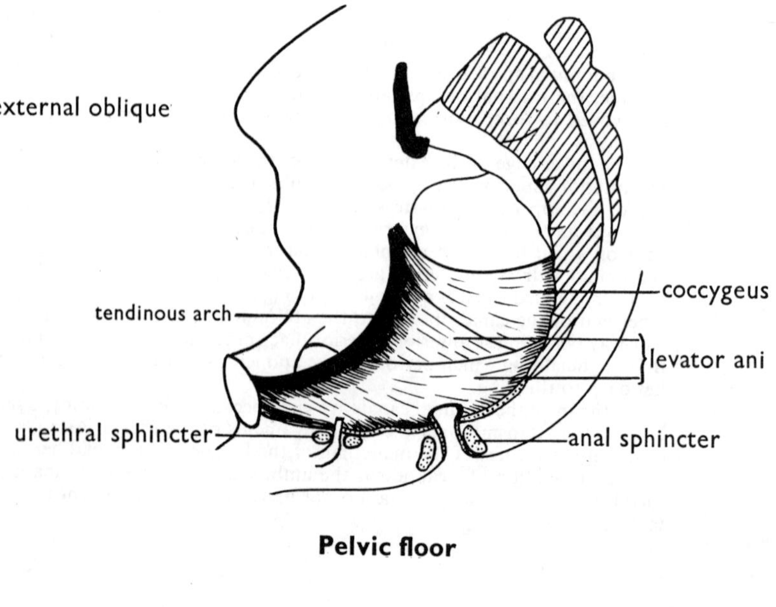

Pelvic floor

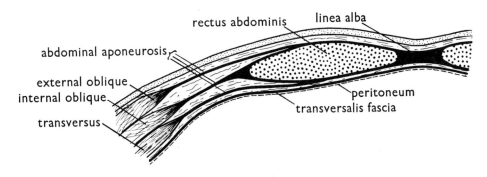

Section of front of abdominal wall above arcuate line

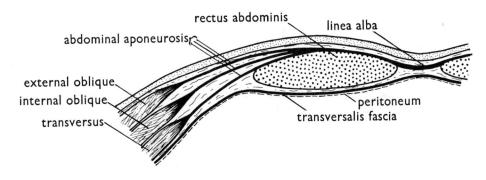

Section of front of abdominal wall below arcuate line

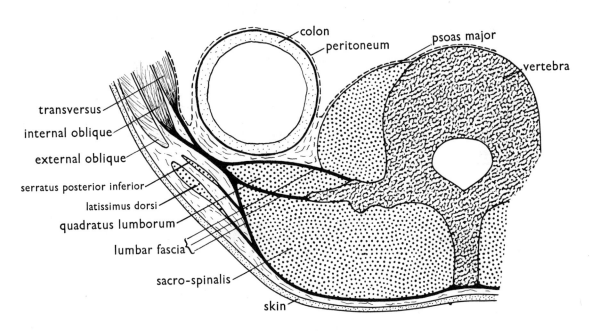

Section of back of abdominal wall

The Diaphragm

The diaphragm is a dome-shaped partition between the thoracic and abdominal cavities (see page 75). It is formed of radially arranged muscle fibres which take origin from the sternum, the ribs, the costal cartilages, the arcuate ligaments and the lumbar vertebrae and which are inserted on to a central tendon. The sternal and costal parts of the diaphragm and the fibres from the arcuate ligaments are spread out into flat sheets, but the parts originating from the vertebrae form two pillars called the **crura**. The left crus is the shorter and arises from the second lumbar vertebra, while the right crus arises from the third.

Simultaneous contraction of all these muscles pulls down the central tendon and reduces the concavity of the diaphragm thus increasing the capacity of the thorax. This produces suction in the thoracic cavity which draws air into the lungs during inspiration. Contraction of the diaphragm also precedes all expulsive actions, e.g. coughing, vomiting, micturition, defaecation and parturition.

The upper surface of the diaphragm is covered by parts of the parietal pleura and pericardium, while the lower surface is covered with peritoneum and has the liver suspended from it by the falciform ligament—see page 75.

The Muscles of Respiration

A great many muscles are involved in the production of the respiratory movements. They not only produce the movements but also steady the adjacent parts. Only the most important are quoted below. (See also page 88.)

(a) **Quiet inspiration** involves the **diaphragm**, the **external** and **internal intercostals** and **levatores costarum**, and the **quadratus lumborum** and **serratus posterior inferior** muscles.

The whole dome of the diaphragm is pulled down till it presses on the viscera. Further downward movement is resisted by the tone of the abdominal muscles and continued contraction then causes the sternum to be moved forwards as the dome flattens. This movement is assisted by the intercostals and levatores costarum which raise and slightly rotate the ribs. The quadratus lumborum and serratus posterior inferior muscles fix the lower ribs and therefore hold the lower edge of the diaphragm in place.

(b) **Deep inspiration** involves, in addition to the above, the **scaleni, sternomastoid** and **serratus posterior superior** muscles which assist the raising of the ribs and sternum, and the **sacro-spinalis** which flattens the back.

(c) **Forced inspiration** involves, in addition to the above, the **serratus anterior** and **pectoralis minor** muscles which assist the raising of the ribs while the scapulae are fixed by the **trapezius, levator scapulae** and **rhomboideus** muscles. When the arms are fixed in the raised position the **pectoralis major** also helps inspiration.

(d) **Quiet expiration** is caused mainly by elastic recoil assisted by the normal tone of the **abdominal wall** pressing the viscera against the under side of the diaphragm and by the **sternocostalis** muscles depressing the ribs.

(e) **Forced expiration** involves the strong contraction of all the muscles of the **abdominal wall** which force the viscera against the diaphragm and thus increase the concavity of the dome. In addition the **latissimus dorsi** and **serratus posterior inferior** muscles help to depress the ribs while at the same time the vertebral column is flexed.

The Openings of the Diaphragm

The diaphragm is perforated to allow the passage of structures between the thorax and the abdomen. The three chief openings are:

1. the *aortic* opening which transmits the **aorta** and the **thoracic duct,**
2. the *oesophageal* opening which transmits the **oesophagus** and the **vagus** nerves,
3. the *vena caval* opening which transmits the **inferior vena cava.**

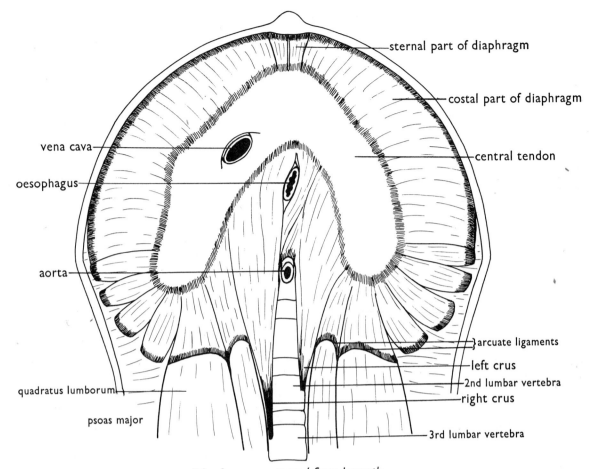

sternal part of diaphragm

costal part of diaphragm

vena cava

central tendon

oesophagus

aorta

arcuate ligaments

left crus

2nd lumbar vertebra

right crus

quadratus lumborum

psoas major

3rd lumbar vertebra

Diaphragm—*viewed from beneath*

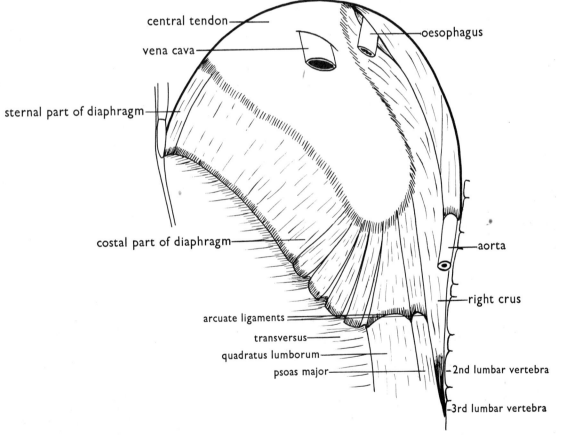

central tendon

oesophagus

vena cava

sternal part of diaphragm

aorta

costal part of diaphragm

right crus

arcuate ligaments

transversus

quadratus lumborum

psoas major

2nd lumbar vertebra

3rd lumbar vertebra

Diaphragm—*right half viewed from the side*

THE NERVOUS SYSTEM

The nervous system deals with the rapid conduction of messages in the form of electrical impulses from one part of the body to another and the coordination of the body's activities. It is formed of specially sensitive cells called **neurones**, supported by **neuroglial** cells and so arranged that they make up a **central nervous system** consisting of the **brain**, the **spinal cord**, a **peripheral system** of the **nerves** and the **ganglia**.

NEURONES

There are three types of neurone, in each of which the impulses pass towards the cell body or **cyton** in the **dendron** (dendrons) and away from it in the **axon**.

The bipolar and unipolar neurones are sensory, receiving stimuli and passing the impulses generated to the brain and spinal cord, while multipolar neurones are found making connections and passing impulses out to the various parts of the body which react to them.

The cell bodies of the neurones are always massed in groups, either in the **grey matter** of the brain and spinal cord, or in groups called **ganglia**. The superficial grey matter of the brain is called **cortex**, while deeper masses are called **nuclei**.

The principal processes or fibres may be **medullated** or **non-medullated**.

The medullary sheath is made of fatty material called lecithin. It insulates the axis cylinder, which is the conducting path. Most fibres associated with sensation and voluntary motor reaction have such a sheath and appear white. Post-ganglionic fibres associated with involuntary reaction, and some pain fibres, are non-medullated and appear grey.

Every peripheral nerve fibre is sheathed in **neurilemma**. This is formed from neuroglial cells the nuclei of which lie close beneath the sheath whether the nerve fibre is medullated or not. Many of the neurones which lie completely inside the central nervous system are without neurilemma. Thus in the grey matter there are many naked dendrons and axons without either medullary sheath or neurilemma, simply supported by a meshwork of neuroglial cells.

Functionally the neurones are classified as follows:

1. Sensory or afferent neurones which receive stimuli and pass impulses to the spinal cord and brain,

2. Association neurones which relay impulses,

3. Motor or efferent neurones which pass impulses from the brain and spinal cord, ultimately to affect the muscles and glands.

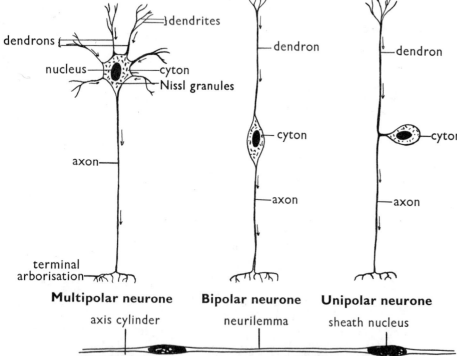

Multipolar neurone   **Bipolar neurone**   **Unipolar neurone**

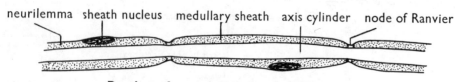

Portion of a non-medullated nerve fibre

Portion of a medullated nerve fibre

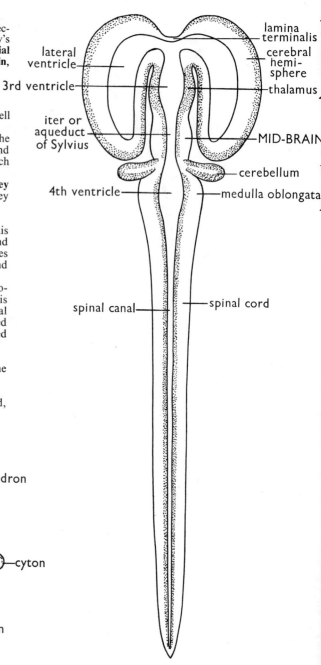

Diagram of the derivatives of the neural tube

THE CENTRAL NERVOUS SYSTEM

The central nervous system develops from a continuous tube-like structure composed of cells which become the nervous tissue of the brain and spinal cord. It has a continuous canal which becomes distended into the ventricles of the brain.

The brain itself originates as three swellings or vesicles in the head region which are known as the fore-brain, mid-brain and hind-brain rudiments respectively. Each of these becomes complicated as development proceeds but fore-, mid- and hind-brain regions can always be recognised.

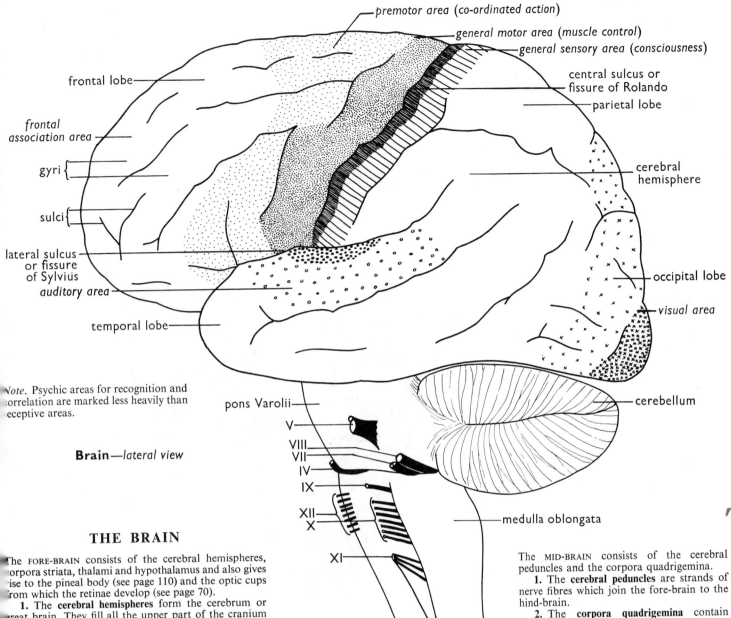

premotor area (co-ordinated action)
general motor area (muscle control)
general sensory area (consciousness)
central sulcus or fissure of Rolando
parietal lobe
cerebral hemisphere
occipital lobe
visual area
cerebellum
medulla oblongata

frontal lobe
frontal association area
gyri
sulci
lateral sulcus or fissure of Sylvius
auditory area
temporal lobe
pons Varolii
V
VIII
VII
IV
IX
XII
X
XI

Note. Psychic areas for recognition and correlation are marked less heavily than receptive areas.

Brain—*lateral view*

THE BRAIN

The FORE-BRAIN consists of the cerebral hemispheres, corpora striata, thalami and hypothalamus and also gives rise to the pineal body (see page 110) and the optic cups from which the retinae develop (see page 70).

1. The **cerebral hemispheres** form the cerebrum or great brain. They fill all the upper part of the cranium and their parts are named after the bones under which they lie, frontal lobes, parietal lobes, occipital lobes and temporal lobes. The two hemispheres are joined together by the corpus callosum and the fornix. The surface of each hemisphere is convoluted to allow a greater area for the cerebral cortex, which consists of grey matter containing many neurones and is responsible for consciousness and memory. Areas with special functions have been mapped out.

2. The **corpora striata** or **basal ganglia** develop in the central parts of the hemispheres and are not visible externally. They include the caudate and lentiform nuclei and are nerve centres concerned with the modification of motor function. Close to the thalami lie the **red nuclei**.

3. The **thalami** form the side walls of the third ventricle. They are joined together by the interthalamic connection and are important relay centres for the sensory nerve tracts on their way to the corpora striata, cerebral cortex and hypothalamus.

4. The **hypothalamus** forms the floor of the third ventricle. It is made up of the optic chiasma (see page 56), the infundibulum (see page 108), the corpora mamillaria and a number of small nuclei which include the highest autonomic nerve centres (see page 62).

The roof of the third ventricle is largely non-nervous forming the pineal body and a **choroid plexus**. The latter consists of a network of blood vessels in a sheet of connective tissue. It extends into the lateral ventricles.

The MID-BRAIN consists of the cerebral peduncles and the corpora quadrigemina.

1. The **cerebral peduncles** are strands of nerve fibres which join the fore-brain to the hind-brain.

2. The **corpora quadrigemina** contain relay centres connected with visual and auditory stimuli.

The HIND-BRAIN consists of the cerebellum, pons Varolii and the medulla oblongata.

1. The **cerebellum** or lesser brain lies behind and beneath the cerebrum and like the latter has two hemispheres. It is highly complex and its surface is convoluted to increase the amount of cortex. Its central strands constitute the arbor vitae and it is connected to the rest of the brain by three pairs of peduncles.

(a) The superior cerebellar peduncles contain tracts to the red nuclei and thalami of the opposite sides, from which there are connections to the cerebral cortex. Anterior spino-cerebellar tracts lie close to them and contain fibres from the spinal cord.

(b) The inferior cerebellar peduncles contain tracts from the medulla and spinal cord.

(c) The middle cerebellar peduncles encircle the cerebral peduncles to form the pons Varolii.

2. The **pons Varolii** contains the nuclei pontis, in which tracts from the cerebral cortex connect with tracts to the cerebellar hemisphere of the opposite side; and it also contains the nuclei of origin of some of the cranial nerves.

3. The **medulla oblongata** or spinal bulb is in many ways like an enlarged region of the spinal cord, with which it is continuous. Inside the medulla the majority of the descending or motor nerve tracts cross from one side to the other (decussate) forming the pyramidal tracts and there are the nuclei of origin of several of the cranial nerves. The latter include the special centres controlling rate of heart beat, rate and depth of breathing, swallowing and vomiting.

The cavity of the fourth ventricle lies in the medulla but its roof is formed partly of the cerebellum and partly by a **choroid plexus** consisting of a network of blood vessels in a sheet of connective tissue. The roof is perforated by the foramen of Magendie which allows cerebro-spinal fluid from inside the brain to pass out into the theca (see page 58).

Note. The mid-brain, pons Varolii and medulla oblongata together form the **brain stem**.

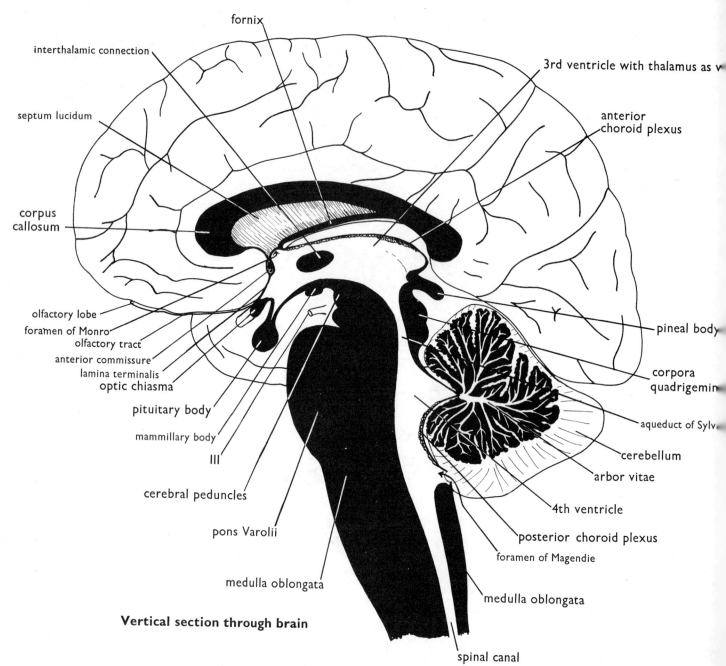

fornix

interthalamic connection

3rd ventricle with thalamus as w

septum lucidum

anterior
choroid plexus

corpus
callosum

olfactory lobe

foramen of Monro

olfactory tract

anterior commissure

lamina terminalis

optic chiasma

pituitary body

mammillary body

III

cerebral peduncles

pons Varolii

medulla oblongata

pineal body

corpora
quadrigemin

aqueduct of Sylv

cerebellum

arbor vitae

4th ventricle

posterior choroid plexus

foramen of Magendie

medulla oblongata

spinal canal

Vertical section through brain

THE CRANIAL NERVES

There are twelve pairs of cranial nerves attached to the brain stem at different levels. Some of these nerves contain sensory fibres only and some motor fibres only, while the remainder are mixed nerves but have separate sensory and motor roots. The first two cranial nerves differ from the rest in being non-segmental in origin—i.e. not related to the embryological segmentation of the head.

All the sensory nerves have ganglia outside the brain, while all the motor nerves originate from nuclei inside the brain.

No.	Name	Distribution
I	Olfactory	Sensory nerves of smell from the nose
II	Optic	Sensory nerves of sight from the eyes. Many fibres cross in the optic chiasma
III	Oculomotor	Motor nerves to the superior, inferior and medial rectus and inferior oblique muscles of the eye
IV	Trochlear	Motor nerves to the superior oblique muscles of the eyes
V	Trigeminal (three branches)	Ophthalmic—sensory nerves from above and around the orbits and parts of the nasal cavities Maxillary—sensory nerves from around and below the orbits and from upper jaw and teeth Mandibular—sensory nerves from lower part of face, lower jaw and teeth and from temples and pinnae; also motor nerves to the muscles of mastication

CONTINUED ON PAGE 57

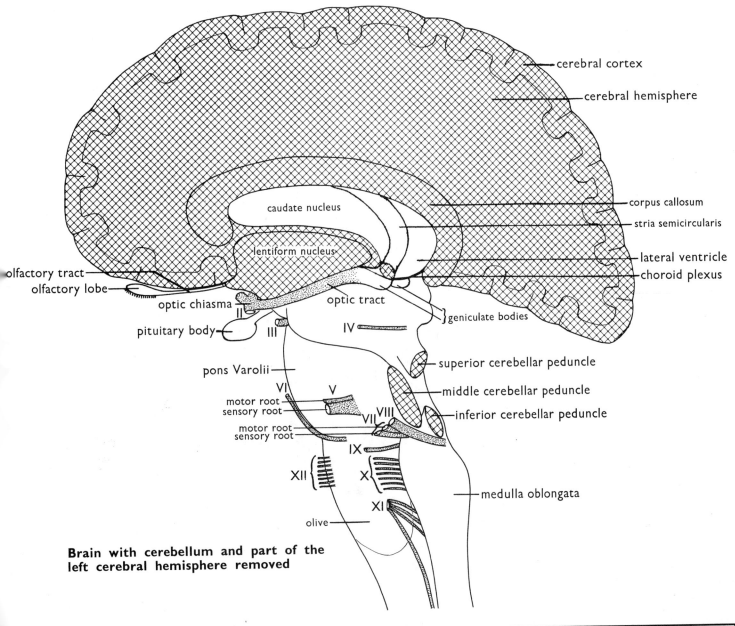

cerebral cortex

cerebral hemisphere

corpus callosum

stria semicircularis

lateral ventricle

choroid plexus

caudate nucleus

lentiform nucleus

olfactory tract

olfactory lobe

optic chiasma

pituitary body

optic tract

geniculate bodies

superior cerebellar peduncle

middle cerebellar peduncle

inferior cerebellar peduncle

pons Varolii

motor root
sensory root

motor root
sensory root

medulla oblongata

olive

Brain with cerebellum and part of the left cerebral hemisphere removed

The Cranial Nerves
(continued)

No.	Name	Distribution
VI	Abducent	Motor nerves to the lateral rectus muscles of the eyes
VII	Facial	Sensory nerves of taste from the anterior part of the tongue Motor nerves to the muscles of expression, the scalp, pinnae and neck
VIII	Auditory *(two branches)*	Cochlear—nerves of hearing from the cochlea Vestibular—nerves of balance from the semicircular canals and vestibule
IX	Glosso-pharyngeal	Sensory nerves of taste from the posterior part of the tongue and from the pharynx Motor nerves to the muscles of the pharynx and to the parotid gland
X	Vagus	Sensory nerves from the larynx, trachea, lungs, oesophagus, stomach, intestines, gall bladder and large arteries and veins. Motor nerves consisting chiefly of autonomic fibres to the pharynx, larynx, trachea, oesophagus, stomach, small intestine, pancreas, liver, spleen, ascending colon, kidneys, heart and visceral blood vessels
XI	Accessory *(two parts)*	Cranial—motor nerves joining the vagus to supply the pharynx and larynx Spinal—motor nerves arising from the spinal cord and entering the skull, then leaving it again to the muscles of the neck
XII	Hypoglossal	Motor nerves to the muscles of the tongue and hyoid region

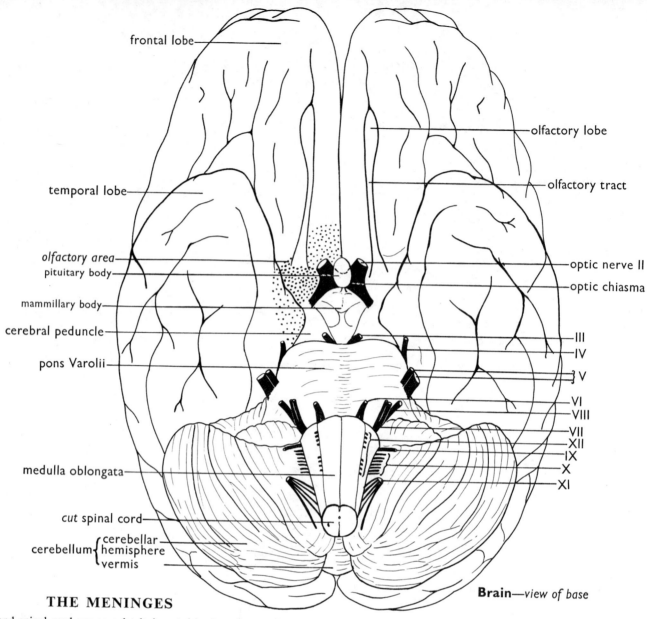

frontal lobe

olfactory lobe

temporal lobe

olfactory tract

olfactory area
pituitary body

optic nerve II
optic chiasma

mammillary body

cerebral peduncle

III
IV

pons Varolii

V

VI
VIII
VII
XII
IX
X
XI

medulla oblongata

cut spinal cord

cerebellum { cerebellar hemisphere
vermis

Brain—*view of base*

THE MENINGES

The brain and spinal cord are completely invested in three layers of tissue called the meninges.

1. The **dura mater** is the tough fibrous outermost layer. It lines the bones of the cranium and the canal formed by the vertebrae. It forms also the **falx cerebri** between the cerebral hemispheres and the **tentorium cerebelli** separating the cerebral hemispheres from the cerebellum. The main venous sinuses inside the cranium lie in the dura mater (see page 96).

2. The **arachnoid mater** is a delicate membrane separated from the dura mater by the subdural space in which there is a thin film of serous fluid. It encloses the subarachnoid space, which is traversed by fine trabeculae of connective tissue and which contains cerebro-spinal fluid and the larger blood vessels of the brain.

3. The **pia mater** is the very delicate inner membrane which closely invests the brain and spinal cord and supports a network of fine blood vessels, including those of the choroid plexuses which roof the ventricles. It follows every convolution of the surface of the nervous tissue and sheaths the roots of the cranial and spinal nerves.

THE CEREBRO-SPINAL FLUID

Cerebro-spinal fluid is secreted by the choroid plexuses and is of the same general composition as lymph (see page 102). It fills the cavities of the brain and spinal cord and passes through the openings in the roof of the 4th ventricle to fill the subarachnoid spaces also. Little fluid enters the spinal region, where constancy of composition is maintained by diffusion and by alteration of posture; but there is a distinct, though slow, flow into the cranial region, where the fluid re-enters the blood through the arachnoid villi, which are small papillae projecting into the superior sagittal blood sinus.

The functions of the cerebro-spinal fluid are:

1. to support the delicate nervous tissue, **2.** to protect it against shock, **3.** to maintain a uniform pressure around it, **4.** to supply it with food by direct bathing of the cells in parts where no blood vessels penetrate.

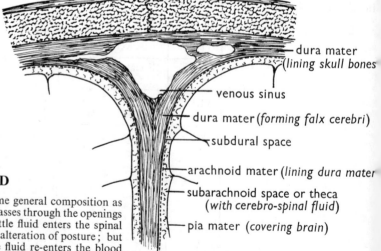

dura mater
(*lining skull bones*

venous sinus

dura mater (*forming falx cerebri*)

subdural space

arachnoid mater (*lining dura mater*

subarachnoid space or theca
(*with cerebro-spinal fluid*)

pia mater (*covering brain*)

Meninges

THE SPINAL CORD

The spinal cord lies in the canal formed by the neural arches of the vertebrae. In the three-month-old foetus it stretches from the foramen magnum to the lower end of the canal, but it grows more slowly than the vertebral column and therefore in the adult it reaches only to the upper margin of the second lumbar vertebra and is connected to the lower end of the canal by the non-nervous **filum terminale**. The average length of the cord is about 430 mm and thickness about 20 mm, but it has two wider parts, the cervical and lumbar enlargements, where the nerves to the limbs originate.

There is a fine central canal throughout the cord continuous with the ventricles of the brain and like them filled with cerebro-spinal fluid. The grey matter lies around this canal and extends as two posterior and two anterior horns in which there are cell bodies of association and motor neurones respectively. (*Note:* sensory neurones have their cell bodies outside the cord.) The white matter lies external to the grey matter and forms ascending and descending tracts of fibres through which messages are passed up and down the cord to different levels and to and from the brain.

The functions of the spinal cord are:
1. to relay impulses coming in and going out at the same level,
2. to relay impulses up and down the cord to other levels,
3. to relay impulses to and from the brain.

THE SPINAL NERVES

There are thirty-one pairs of spinal nerves, each of which is attached to the spinal cord by a **posterior** or **sensory root**, on which there is a **ganglion** containing the cell bodies of the sensory nerve fibres, and an **anterior** or **motor root** without ganglion. The two roots join where the nerves leave the spinal canal. The mixed nerves so formed soon divide into posterior and anterior branches or rami. The posterior primary rami are small and serve the skin and muscles of the back. The anterior primary rami are larger and have a varied distribution to the skin and muscles of the sides and front of the trunk and of the limbs. Many of the anterior branches from complicated plexuses by means of which fibres from different levels of the cord can serve the same region of the body.

Because of the shortness of the spinal cord the lumbar and sacral nerves have to pass for some distance down the vertebral canal before emerging segmentally. The bundle of nerves so formed is called the **cauda equina.**

Note. The plexuses are extremely complicated but the more important nerves are shaded with dots.

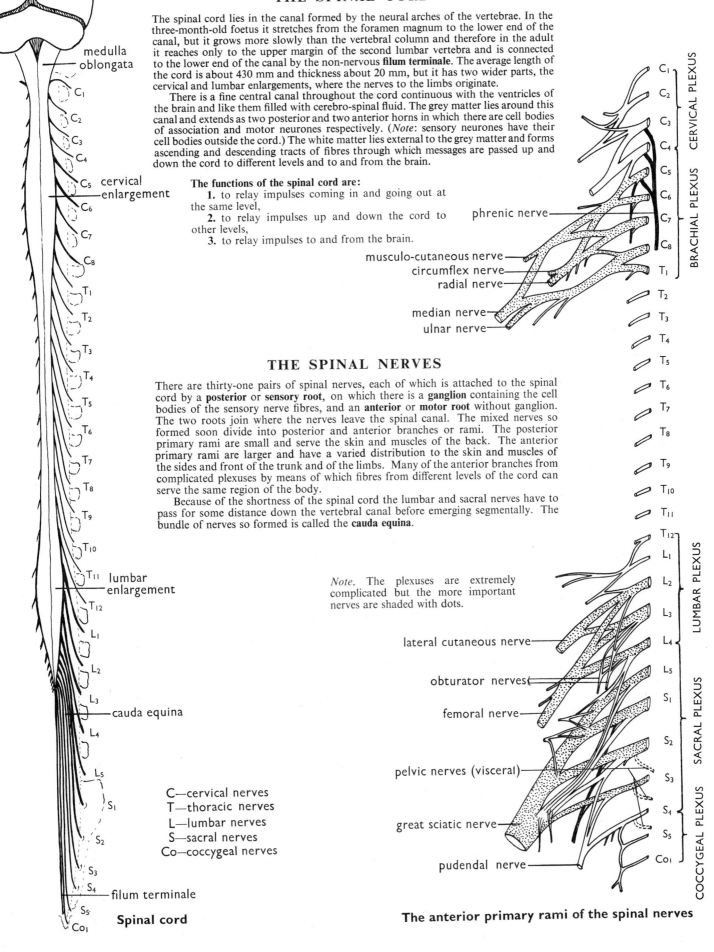

C—cervical nerves
T—thoracic nerves
L—lumbar nerves
S—sacral nerves
Co—coccygeal nerves

Spinal cord

The anterior primary rami of the spinal nerves

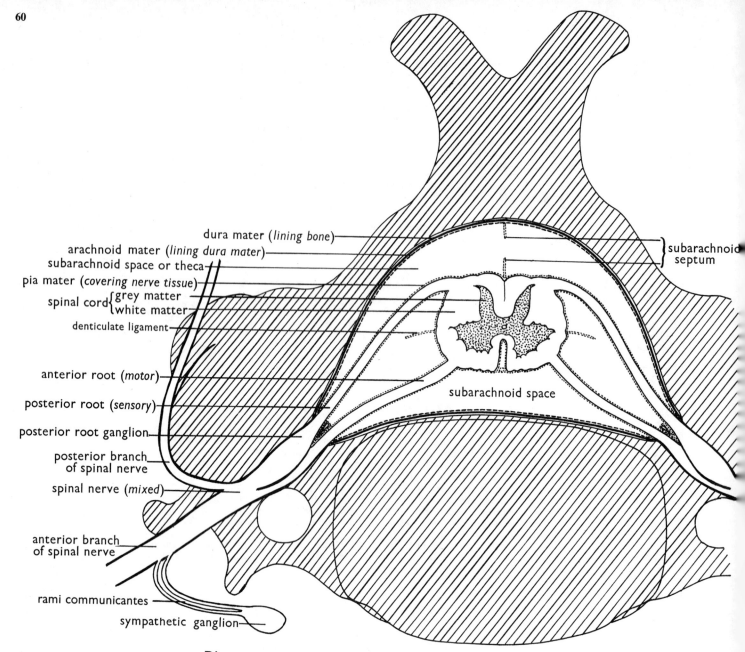

dura mater (*lining bone*)
arachnoid mater (*lining dura mater*)
subarachnoid space or theca
pia mater (*covering nerve tissue*)
spinal cord {grey matter / white matter}
denticulate ligament
anterior root (*motor*)
posterior root (*sensory*)
posterior root ganglion
posterior branch of spinal nerve
spinal nerve (*mixed*)
anterior branch of spinal nerve
rami communicantes
sympathetic ganglion

subarachnoid septum
subarachnoid space

Diagram to show the relationship of the spinal cord and its membranes and of a typical spinal nerve to a vertebra

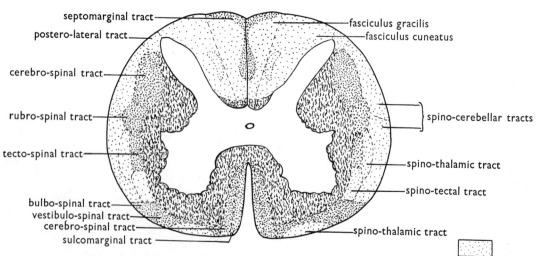

septomarginal tract
postero-lateral tract
cerebro-spinal tract
rubro-spinal tract
tecto-spinal tract
bulbo-spinal tract
vestibulo-spinal tract
cerebro-spinal tract
sulcomarginal tract

fasciculus gracilis
fasciculus cuneatus
spino-cerebellar tracts
spino-thalamic tract
spino-tectal tract
spino-thalamic tract

The arrangement of the nerve tracts in the spinal cord

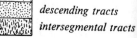

descending tracts
intersegmental tracts

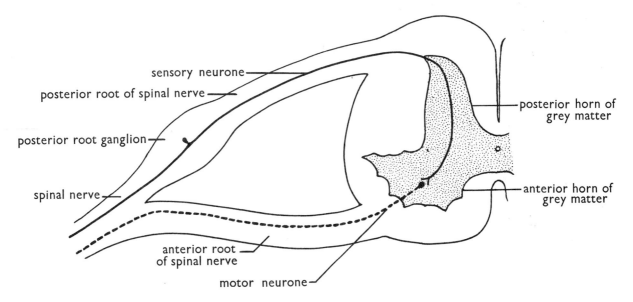

Path of a simple voluntary reflex

Summary of the distribution of cranial and spinal nerves to some of the chief voluntary muscles.

Note.—In the case of spinal nerves, the posterior primary rami are marked (P); the anterior primary rami are unmarked.

Cr=cranial; C=cervical; T=thoracic; L=lumbar; S=sacral.

Muscles	Nerves
Adductor brevis and longus	obturator L2 and L3
Adductor magnus	sciatic L4
Anal sphincter	pudendal L4
Anconeus	radial C7 and C8
Biceps brachii	musculocutaneous C5 and C6
Biceps femoris	sciatic (medial and lateral popliteal branches) L5–S3
Brachialis	musculocutaneous C5 and C6
Brachioradialis	radial C5 and C6
Coccygeus	S4 and S5
Constrictors of pharynx	glossopharyngeal (pharyngeal plexus) Cr9
Coracobrachialis	musculocutaneous C7
Deltoid	circumflex C5 and C6
Diaphragm	phrenic C3–C5 and T6 or T7 or T7–T12
Extensors of fingers	interosseus C7
Extensors of toes	sciatic (lateral popliteal branch) L5 and S1
Extensors of wrist	radial C6 and C7 and median C7
External oblique	T7–T12
Facial expression muscles	facial Cr7
Flexors of fingers	median C7 and C8
Flexors of toes	sciatic (medial popliteal branch) L5–S2
Flexors of wrist	median C6 and C7 and ulnar C8
Gastrocnemius	sciatic (medial popliteal branch) L5 and S1
Gemellus inferior	L4–S1
Gemellus superior	L5–S2
Gluteus maximus	inferior gluteal L5–S2
Gluteus medius and minimus	superior gluteal L4 and L5
Gracilis	obturator L3 and L4
Iliacus	femoral L3
Inferior oblique	oculomotor Cr3
Infraspinatus	suprascapular C5
Intercostals	intercostals T1–T11
Internal oblique	T6–L1
Latissimus dorsi	C7 and C8
Levator ani	L4 and pudendal
Levatores costarum	T1–T12 (P)
Levator palpibrae	oculomotor Cr3
Levator scapulae	C3–C5
Masseter	trigeminal (mandibular branch) Cr5
Nasal muscles	facial (upper buccal branch) Cr7
Obturator externus	obturator L3 and L4
Obturator internus	L5–S2
Occipitofrontalis	facial Cr7
Orbicularis oculi	facial (temporal and zygomatic branches) Cr7

Muscles	Nerves
Pectineus	femoral L2 and L3
Pectoralis major	pectoral C6–C8
Pectoralis minor	pectoral C7 and C8
Peroneus	sciatic (lateral popliteal branch) L5 and S1
Piriformis	S1 and S2
Plantaris	sciatic (medial popliteal branch) L5 and S1
Platysma	facial (cervical branch) Cr7
Popliteus	sciatic (medial popliteal branch) L5 and S1
Pronator quadratus	median C8
Pronator teres	median C6
Psoas major	L2 and L3 or L4
Psoas minor	L1
Pterygoid	trigeminal (mandibular branch) Cr5
Pyramidalis	subcostal T12
Quadratus femoris	L4–S1
Quadratus lumborum	T12–L3 or L4
Quadriceps femoris	femoral L3 and L4
Rectus abdominis	T6 or T7–T12
Rectus externus, internus and superior	oculomotor Cr3
Rectus inferior	abducens Cr6
Rhomboideus major and minor	C5
Sacro-spinalis	lower C, all T and upper L (P)
Sartorius	femoral L2 and L3
Scalenus	C4–C8
Semimembranosus	sciatic (medial popliteal branch) L4 and L5
Semitendinosus	sciatic (medial popliteal branch) L5–S2
Serratus anterior	C5–C7
Serratus posterior inferior	T9–T12
Serratus posterior superior	T2–T5
Soleus	sciatic (medial popliteal branch) L5–S2
Sternomastoid	accessory Cr11 and C2
Subclavius	C5 and C6
Subscapularis	subscapular C6
Superior oblique	trochlear Cr4
Supinator	interosseus C5 and C6
Supraspinatus	C5
Temporalis	trigeminal (mandibular branch) Cr5
Tensor fasciae latae	superior gluteal L4–S1
Teres major	subscapular C6
Teres minor	circumflex C5
Tibialis anterior	sciatic (lateral popliteal branch) L4 and L5
Tibialis posterior	sciatic (medial popliteal branch) L4 and L5
Tongue muscles	hypoglossal Cr12
Transversus	T6–L1
Trapezius	accessory Cr11 and C3–C4
Triceps	radial C7
Urethral sphincter	pudendal S2–S4

THE AUTONOMIC NERVOUS SYSTEM

In addition to the ordinary motor fibres, many of the cranial and spinal nerves contain autonomic fibres which control involuntary muscles and glands. The autonomic system is in two parts.

1. The **cranio-sacral** or **parasympathetic system** consists of fibres which accompany the third, seventh and ninth cranial nerves, form the greater part of the tenth cranial nerves and accompany the second, third and fourth sacral nerves. All these fibres relay through ganglia in the smooth muscle or the glands served. The post-ganglionic fibres are therefore very short and enable the individual glands and muscles to act independently.

2. The **thoracico-lumbar** or **sympathetic system** consists of fibres which accompany the thoracic and first, second and third lumbar nerves and relay through sympathetic ganglia in two chains, one on either side of the aorta. From these chains there are networks of fibres to the viscera, with further ganglia in the mesenteries, and there are also very long post-ganglionic fibres accompanying the main peripheral nerves to the blood vessels and to the skin. The connections between the sympathetic cords and the spinal nerves are called rami communicantes. The system tends to act as a whole, producing a mass effect, because each pre-ganglionic fibre relays to a large number of post-ganglionic ones through the ganglia and plexuses.

The effects of the parasympathetic and sympathetic systems are antagonistic. Whereas the parasympathetic system helps to create the internal conditions found during rest, sleep and digestion, the sympathetic system prepares the body for 'flight or fight' and acts in conjunction with adrenaline secreted by the adrenal medulla (see page 109).

Parts affected	Para-sympathetic	Sympathetic	General result
Pupils	contracted	dilated	controls the amount of light entering the eyes
Ciliary muscles	contracted	relaxed	controls accommodation of the eye
Blood vessels	arterioles of glands and viscera dilated	Arterioles of alimentary canal and skin constricted; those of skeletal muscles dilated or constricted by different fibres; tone raised in walls of larger vessels	adjusts the blood pressure and the distribution of the blood
Spleen	dilated	constricted	adjusts the quality and quantity of blood in circulation
Heart beat	slowed and weakened	hastened and strengthened	adjusts the rate of the heart according to the blood pressure and varying muscle activity
Bronchioles	constricted	dilated	adjusts ease of breathing to requirements
Sweat glands		activity increased	produces extra sweat in anticipation of heat production during activity
Adrenal medulla		activity increased	reinforces direct effects mentioned above
Peristalsis of the alimentary canal	increased	decreased	controls the speed of passage of food and the rate of digestion.
Sphincters	relaxed	contracted	*Note.* Digestion is slow when body activity is great and vice versa.
Digestive glands	activity increased	activity decreased	

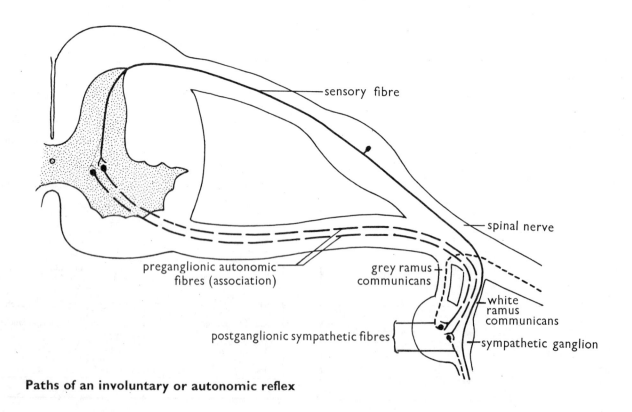

Paths of an involuntary or autonomic reflex

THE METHOD OF FUNCTIONING OF THE NERVOUS SYSTEM

he functioning of the nervous system is exceedingly complex. The pattern of response to stimuli is dependent on the arrangement and interconnections of ie neurones.

Conduction of impulses along the fibres takes place extremely rapidly, but between the processes of adjacent neurones there are small gaps or **synapses** across which the conduction is much slower. The time taken for an impulse to pass is therefore largely dependent on the number of synapses which it has to cross rather than the distance travelled. The impulses are a series of electrical discharges passing in succession along the nerve fibres, while passage across the synapses is performed by minute quantities of chemicals known collectively as **neurotransmitters**. These have considerable specificity and a neurone will respond only if it has the correct receptor protein. **Noradrenaline, seratonin, dopamine** and **enkephalin** have been identified as neurotransmitters.

The neurones are functionally of three types: sensory, motor and association. The latter are arranged to form sensory and motor tracts and nerve centres in the central nervous system. According to the complexity of their connections, there are three levels of behaviour known as archikinetic, paleokinetic and neokinetic.

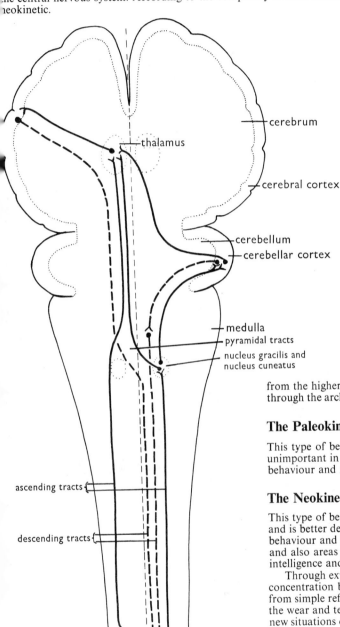

ascending tracts {

descending tracts {

—— sensory paths

– – – motor paths

Diagram to show the more important sensory and motor paths

Labels on diagram: cerebrum, thalamus, cerebral cortex, cerebellum, cerebellar cortex, medulla, pyramidal tracts, nucleus gracilis and nucleus cuneatus, spinal cord

The Archikinetic Level of Behaviour

This is the primitive type of behaviour found in all animals with nervous co-ordination. Its patterns are hereditary and develop independent of environment, intelligence or learning. It is built up of numerous **reflex arcs.**

A simple **reflex arc** consists of (i) a sensory receptor—exteroceptor, proprioceptor or enteroceptor; (ii) a sensory neurone; (iii) a synapse located in the central nervous system; (iv) a motor neurone; and (v) an effector cell—muscle or gland. The actual mechanism is complicated because the motor neurone may be connected to numerous sensory and association neurones so that its response depends on the balance between excitatory and inhibitory impulses reaching it.

The reflexes are classified as:
(a) **intrasegmental reflexes,** when the impulses are passed directly in and out again at the same level of the spinal cord,
(b) **intersegmental reflexes,** when the impulses are passed up or down the spinal cord before being passed out,
(c) **suprasegmental reflexes,** when the impulses are relayed through special centres in the brain—chiefly in the medulla.

The **reflex actions** produced are extremely important in:
1. adjusting the tone of muscles so that their activity is balanced, particularly in posture,
2. producing reciprocal inhibition of antagonistic muscles,
3. producing protective withdrawal and blinking,
4. adjusting the activity of the internal organs to physiological needs.

In many cases the motor path of a reflex arc can be blocked by impulses from the higher nervous centres, but in the absence of such blocking the response to a given stimulus through the archikinetic level is invariable.

The Paleokinetic Level of Behaviour

This type of behaviour is superimposed on the archikinetic type in all vertebrates but is relatively unimportant in man. It is responsible for the very complex patterns of action known as instinctive behaviour and may involve relay of impulses through the corpora striata.

The Neokinetic Level of Behaviour

This type of behaviour is superimposed on the archikinetic type especially in the higher vertebrates and is better developed in man than in any other animal. It is responsible for rational or intelligent behaviour and learning. It involves the cerebral cortex which has special sensory and motor areas and also areas concerned with appreciation of sensation, co-ordination of action, habits, memory, intelligence and emotions.

Through experience and training much of the behaviour which early in life requires thought and concentration becomes a matter of habit. Such habits are called conditioned reflexes. They differ from simple reflexes in that they do not develop to an inevitable pattern. They save the cortex from the wear and tear of perpetual concentration on oft-repeated activities and leave it free to deal with new situations or ideas. The early establishment of conditioned reflexes is very important for mental development.

Note. The cerebellum has archikinetic, paleokinetic and neokinetic regions linked with the other parts of the corresponding systems and essential to their proper functioning.

The Voluntary and Involuntary Systems

For convenience, the nerves serving the parts over which the neokinetic system exerts conscious control are said to be **voluntary**, and those serving the parts over which it has no conscious control are styled **involuntary** or **autonomic**; but these two systems are closely integrated. Both are based on reflex arcs and some of the sensory paths are shared. The highest centres of the autonomic system are in the cerebral cortex and the hypothalamus.

The true difference is that the voluntary or skeletal muscles are stimulated by medullated motor fibres whose cell bodies are inside the brain or spinal cord, while the involuntary or visceral muscles and the glands are stimulated either by non-medullated motor fibres whose cell bodies are in ganglia outside the brain or spinal cord or, in certain cases, by chemicals in the blood (see the endocrine system, page 108).

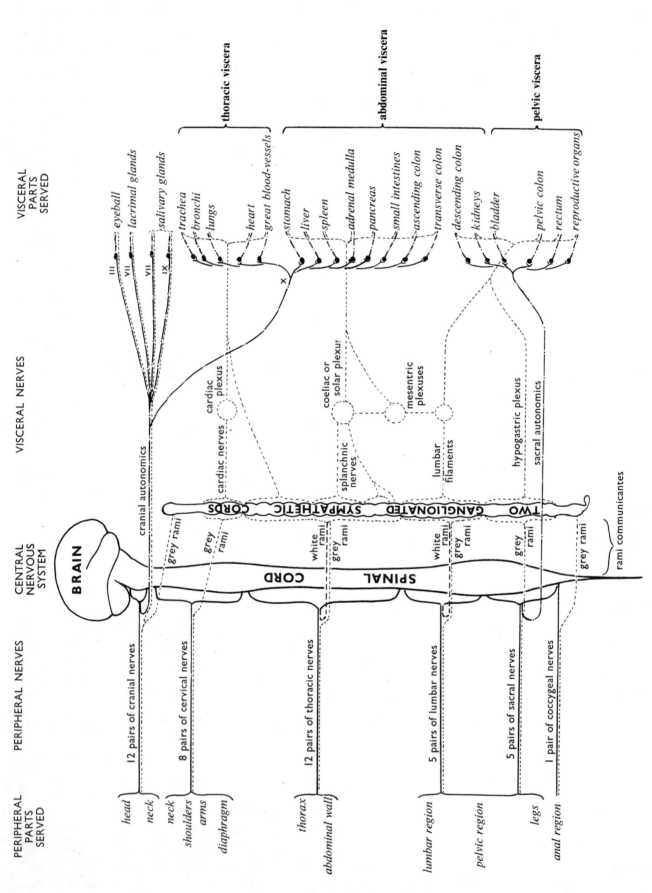

Diagram to show nervous control of the various parts of the body

SENSE ORGANS

Sensory endings are of three types:
1. **exteroceptors,** which sense stimuli from outside the body,
2. **enteroceptors,** which sense stimuli in the viscera,
3. **proprioceptors,** which sense tension in tendons and muscles.

Normally we are not conscious of the stimulation of the enteroceptors and proprioceptors except vaguely (e.g. such feelings as hunger) but excessive stimulation may cause discomfort and pain, which in the case of the enteroceptors is often 'referred' to parts of the body totally different from those receiving the stimuli.

The stimulation of the enteroceptors sets up autonomic reflexes which control such actions as peristalsis of the alimentary canal. The receptors are naked branched fibres.

The stimulation of the proprioceptors sets up reflexes which co-ordinate the action of antagonistic groups of muscles, maintaining posture and tone. The receptors are neurotendinous and neuromuscular sensillae.

The stimulation of the exteroceptors may produce reflex action but whether they do or not we are consciously aware of the stimuli and of their kind and location.

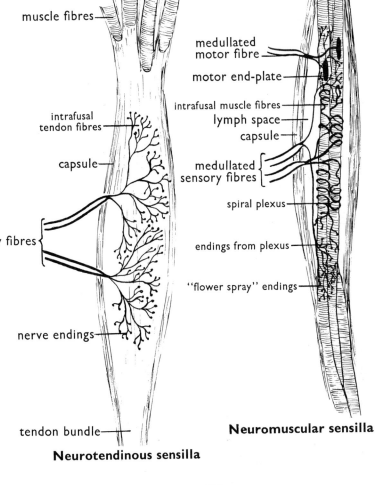

Neuromuscular sensilla

Neurotendinous sensilla

CONSCIOUS SENSATION

The body is conscious of eight distinct types of sensation:
1. touch or pressure,
2. temperature,
3. pain,
4. taste,
5. smell,
6. hearing
7. balance,
8. sight.

Touch, temperature and **pain** receptors are widespread in the skin. The nerve endings may be naked and sense light touch and pain (see page 72), or they may be enveloped in corpuscles, of which there are three main types.

Note. Over-stimulation of any of these types may cause pain. The different sensitivity of different regions of the skin is due to the variation in the abundance of these endings and in the thickness of the epidermis.

Bulbous corpuscle (*cold*)

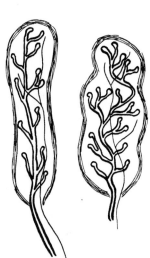

Oval corpuscles (*touch or warmth*)

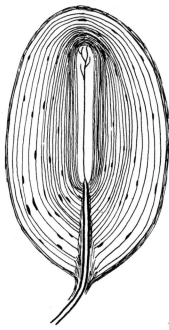

Lamellated corpuscle (*pressure*)

Chemical sensation is of two types distinguished as **taste** and **smell**.

TASTE requires the substance tasted to be in solution and is restricted to the tongue and palate. The taste buds are morphologically all alike but are physiologically differentiated into those sensitive to sweetness, saltness, sourness and bitterness. Each type of taste bud is found on a definite region of the tongue.

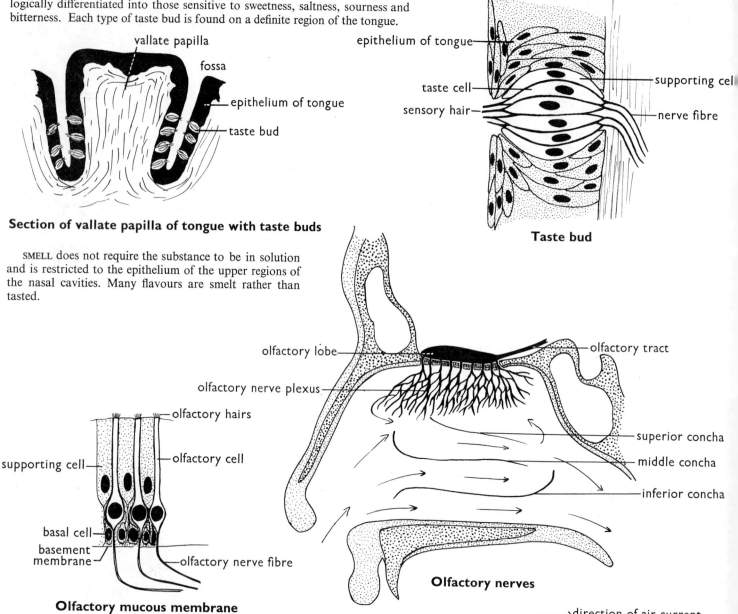

Section of vallate papilla of tongue with taste buds

Taste bud

SMELL does not require the substance to be in solution and is restricted to the epithelium of the upper regions of the nasal cavities. Many flavours are smelt rather than tasted.

Olfactory mucous membrane

Olfactory nerves

⟶ direction of air current

The senses of **hearing** and **balance** are both located in the ears and the sense of **sight** is located in the eyes.

THE EARS

Each ear is divided into three regions, the outer ear, the middle ear and the inner ear.

1. THE OUTER EAR

The outer ear consists of a tube called the external auditory meatus whose inner end is closed by the tympanic membrane and whose outer end is surrounded by the auricle or pinna. The pinna helps to collect sound waves and direct them along the meatus on to the tympanic membrane. The membrane contains many fibres of different lengths so that it vibrates equally to sound waves of different frequencies. The walls of the external auditory meatus have many ceruminous or wax glands, the secretion from which helps to protect the tympanic membrane and keep it pliable.

2. THE MIDDLE EAR

The middle ear consists of the tympanic cavity which communicate with the nasopharynx through the pharyngo-tympanic or Eustachia tube. It contains air to equalise the pressure of the two sides of th tympanic membrane. Across the tympanic cavity is a chain of sma bones called the auditory ossicles (see page 10). These bones relay th sound waves across the cavity. They rock in a lever-like manner an thus decrease the amplitude but increase the power of the vibrations.

3. THE INNER EAR

The inner ear consists of a membranous labyrinth lying in a bon labyrinth of similar shape. The membranous labyrinth is filled wit fluid called endolymph, while the spaces between it and the bon labyrinth are filled with perilymph. The latter is continuous with th cerebro-spinal fluid through the aqueduct of the cochlea.

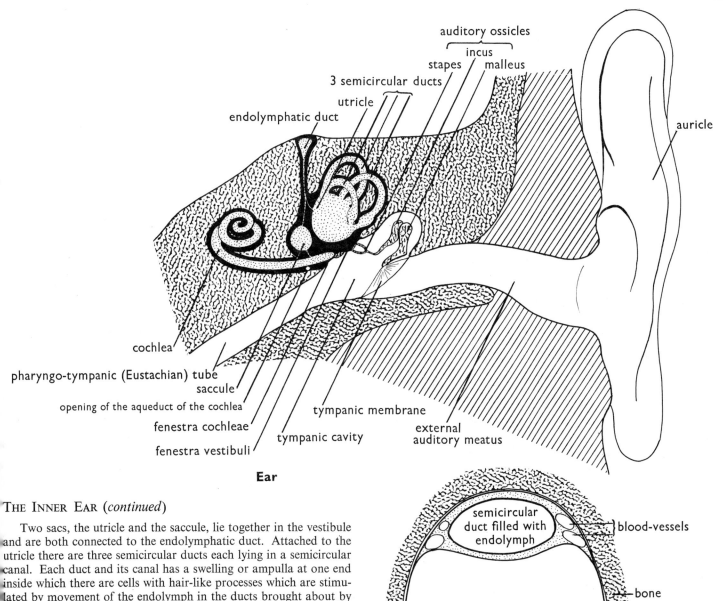

Ear

THE INNER EAR (*continued*)

Two sacs, the utricle and the saccule, lie together in the vestibule and are both connected to the endolymphatic duct. Attached to the utricle there are three semicircular ducts each lying in a semicircular canal. Each duct and its canal has a swelling or ampulla at one end inside which there are cells with hair-like processes which are stimulated by movement of the endolymph in the ducts brought about by movements of the head. The semicircular canals are in mutually perpendicular planes so that movement in every plane can be perceived. The utricle and the saccule also contain patches of sensory hair cells called maculae, which are stimulated by gravitational action on the small crystals of calcium carbonate (otoliths) which adhere to them. The nerve fibres from these cells form the vestibular nerves and the information from impulses in these nerves is interpreted as a sense of balance.

Continuous with the saccule there is a spirally coiled duct called the cochlea, which is the organ of hearing. The sensitive hair cells are arranged on the basilar membrane in the organ of Corti. Their processes are embedded in the tectorial membrane so that when the basilar membrane vibrates they are stimulated. The nerve fibres from these cells form the cochlear nerve.

THE MECHANISM OF HEARING

The accepted theory of the mechanism of hearing is as follows.

The vibrations relayed by the auditory ossicles to the membrane over the fenestra vestibuli cause vibrations in the perilymph which are passed up the scala vestibuli of the cochlea and relayed successively through the vestibular membrane, the scala media, the basilar membrane and the scala tympani. The membrane over the fenestra cochleae at the end of the scala tympani allows equalisation of pressure.

Section of semicircular duct and canal

The basilar membrane contains many fibres which vary in length and thickness according to the region of the cochlea. Each fibre resonates to vibrations of particular wave length. Only where such resonance is taking place is the movement of the basilar membrane sufficient to stimulate the hair cells. Thus sounds of different pitch are sensed by different regions of the organ of Corti. The slight difference in time of arrival of the sound-waves at the two ears is appreciated by the brain as a sense of direction of the source of the sound.

68

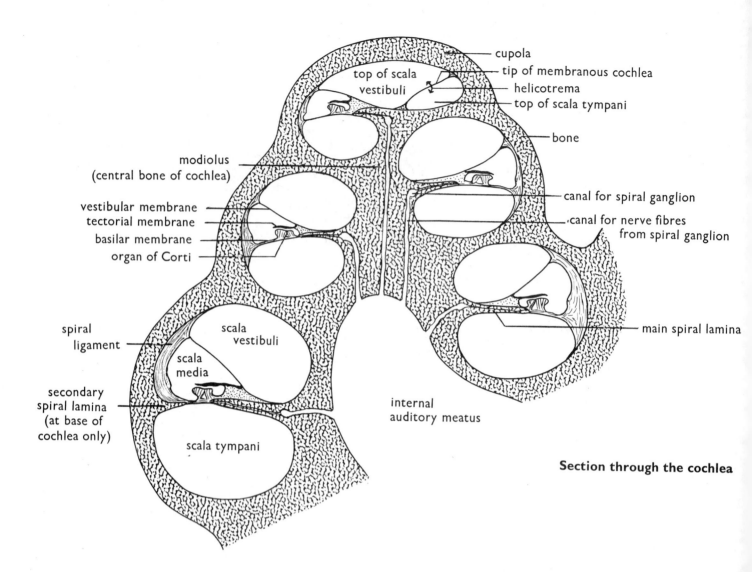

cupola
top of scala vestibuli
tip of membranous cochlea
helicotrema
top of scala tympani
bone

modiolus (central bone of cochlea)

canal for spiral ganglion

vestibular membrane
tectorial membrane
basilar membrane
organ of Corti

canal for nerve fibres from spiral ganglion

spiral ligament

scala vestibuli

scala media

secondary spiral lamina (at base of cochlea only)

main spiral lamina

internal auditory meatus

scala tympani

Section through the cochlea

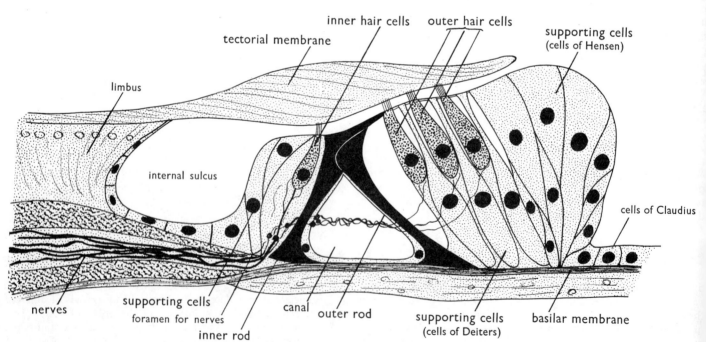

inner hair cells   outer hair cells
tectorial membrane
supporting cells (cells of Hensen)

limbus

internal sulcus

cells of Claudius

nerves
supporting cells
foramen for nerves
inner rod
canal   outer rod
supporting cells (cells of Deiters)
basilar membrane

Section of organ of Corti

THE EYES

nsitivity to light is found only in special cells in the eyes. The greater part of the eye structure is designed to produce a clear image focused on a
:een of these cells.

The eyes lie in bony sockets, the **orbits**. Each eye is held in place and moved by four **rectus** and two **oblique muscles**. The back of the orbit
tween these muscles is filled with fat. The front of the eye is covered with thin transparent skin called **conjunctiva** which also lines the eye-
s. The **lids** contain muscles by which they can be moved, and are fringed with hairs. Special sebaceous glands, the **tarsal glands**, secrete fluid to
ep the lids from sticking together. A **lacrimal gland** lies in the outer corner of each orbit and opens by several ducts under the upper lid. The
rimal secretion bathes and cleans the conjunctiva and normally evaporates. Excess secretion is drained away through the **puncta lacrimalia**, the
rimal ducts and the **naso-lacrimal ducts** into the nasal cavities behind the inferior nasal conchae; or it overflows to produce tears.

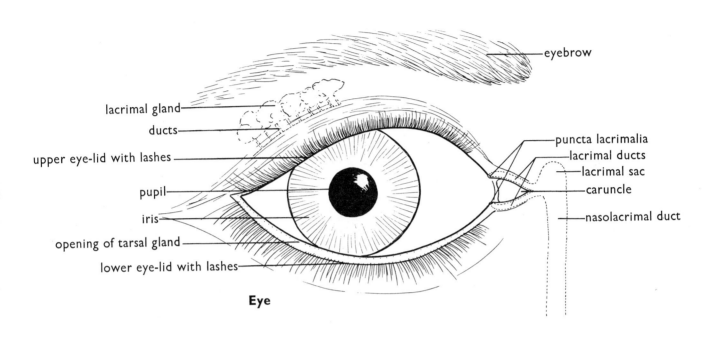

Eye

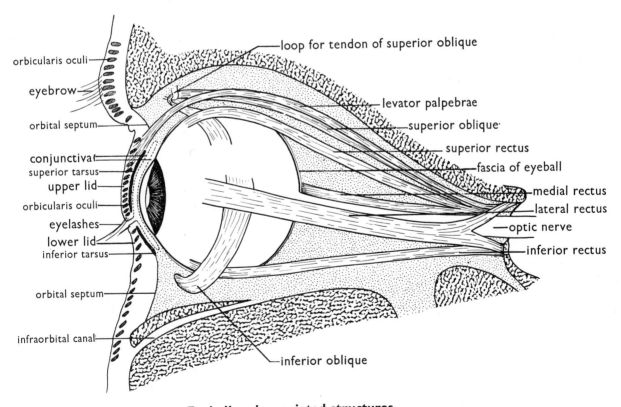

Eyeball and associated structures

THE EYEBALL

Each eyeball is approximately spherical but the front has a smaller radius of curvature than the rest and therefore bulges slightly. The wall of the eyeball is composed of three layers of tissue; the **sclerotic** layer, the **choroid** layer, and the **retinal** layer.

1. The **sclerotic** or **fibrous layer** forms a tough outer coat. It is transparent in front, forming the cornea, and opaque behind, forming the sclera into which the rectus and oblique muscles are inserted. It is continuous with the sheath round the optic nerve.

2. The **choroid** or **vascular layer** contains many blood-vessels and some pigment. At the back of the eye it lines the sclera, but in front it is separated from the cornea and forms the iris and the ciliary body with ciliary processes. The **iris** is made opaque by pigment and contains radial and circular muscles which control the diameter of the pupil and thus control the amount of light entering the eye. The **ciliary body** contains circular and meridional muscles which affect the tension on the suspensory ligaments, and thus bring about accommodation of the eye to focus objects at different distances.

3. The **retinal layer** consists of a pigmented layer of cells which lines the choroid right up to the edge of the iris, to prevent reflection of light inside the eyeball, and a nervous layer which lines the back and sides of the eyeball only and ends at the ora serrata. The retina contains the light-sensitive rods and cones. The **rods** contain visual purple or **rhodopsin**, which is bleached by light. This chemical change starts a chain reaction during which the nerve endings are stimulated. Only dim light is necessary to produce this effect and the image is seen in black and white. Rhodopsin is regenerated and used again. The **cones** are concentrated in the region of the **fovea** (on the optic axis) and are of three types, each containing a special **opsin**, activated by wavelengths in the blue, green, and yellow regions of the spectrum respectively. Brighter light is necessary for the stimulation of these opsins, and the whole colour range is appreciated by proportional stimulation.

THE LENS

The lens is formed of layers of transparent cells enclosed in an elastic capsule. It is biconvex and the radii of curvature, and therefore the focus, can be altered by alteration of the tension on the suspensory ligament. At rest the eye is accommodated to focus distant objects but when the ciliary muscles contract the tension is reduced and the lens swells thus bringing nearer objects into focus. The centre of the lens focuses more accurately than the periphery; therefore vision is more accurate when the pupil is small, i.e. in bright light.

Short sight or myopic vision is caused by either too curved a lens or too deep an eyeball. Long sight is caused by either too flat a lens or too shallow an eyeball. Long sight appearing in old age is due to loss of elasticity of the lens. Astigmatism is caused by aberrations in the curvature of the cornea.

THE CAVITY OF THE EYEBALL

The space in front of the lens is filled with watery fluid called aqueous humour. The space behind the lens is largely occupied by the semi-fluid vitreous body which is enclosed by the fine hyaloid membrane. This membrane is continuous down the hyaloid canal and forms part of the suspensory ligament of the lens.

The fluids maintain the shape of the eyeball and assist the lens in the refraction of light rays on to the retina.

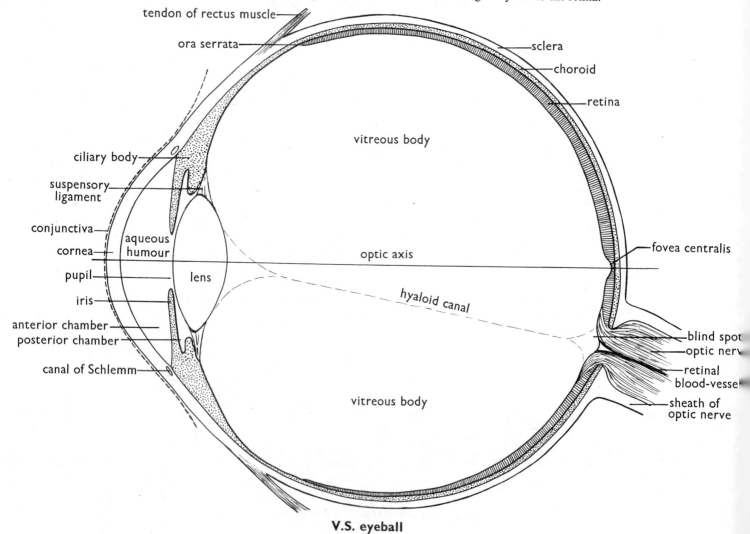

V.S. eyeball

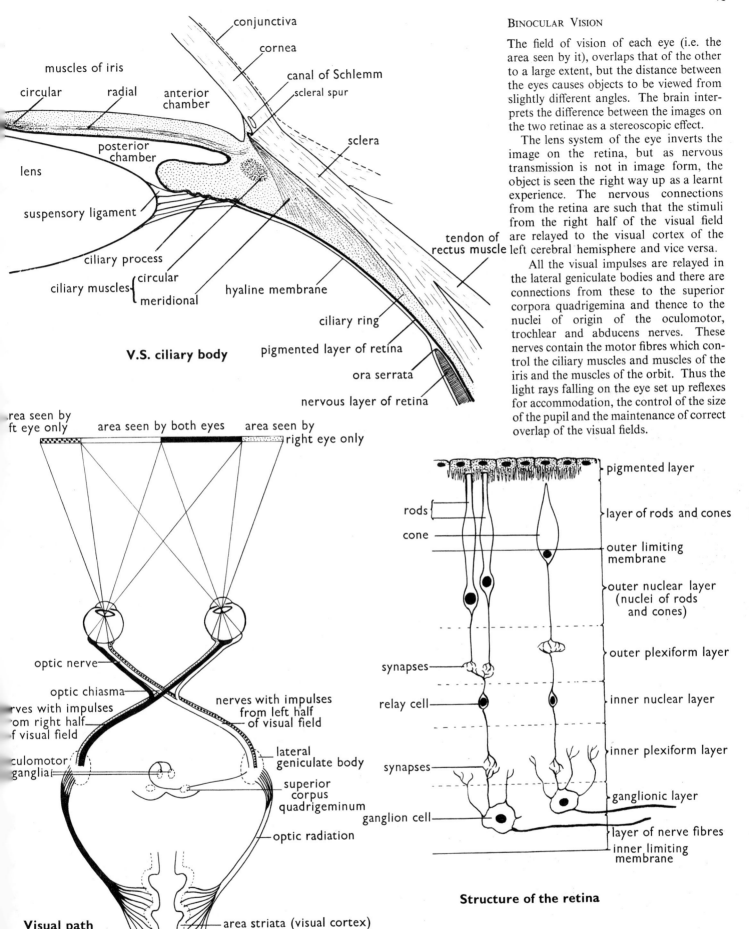

V.S. ciliary body

Visual path

Structure of the retina

BINOCULAR VISION

The field of vision of each eye (i.e. the area seen by it), overlaps that of the other to a large extent, but the distance between the eyes causes objects to be viewed from slightly different angles. The brain interprets the difference between the images on the two retinae as a stereoscopic effect.

The lens system of the eye inverts the image on the retina, but as nervous transmission is not in image form, the object is seen the right way up as a learnt experience. The nervous connections from the retina are such that the stimuli from the right half of the visual field are relayed to the visual cortex of the left cerebral hemisphere and vice versa.

All the visual impulses are relayed in the lateral geniculate bodies and there are connections from these to the superior corpora quadrigemina and thence to the nuclei of origin of the oculomotor, trochlear and abducens nerves. These nerves contain the motor fibres which control the ciliary muscles and muscles of the iris and the muscles of the orbit. Thus the light rays falling on the eye set up reflexes for accommodation, the control of the size of the pupil and the maintenance of correct overlap of the visual fields.

72

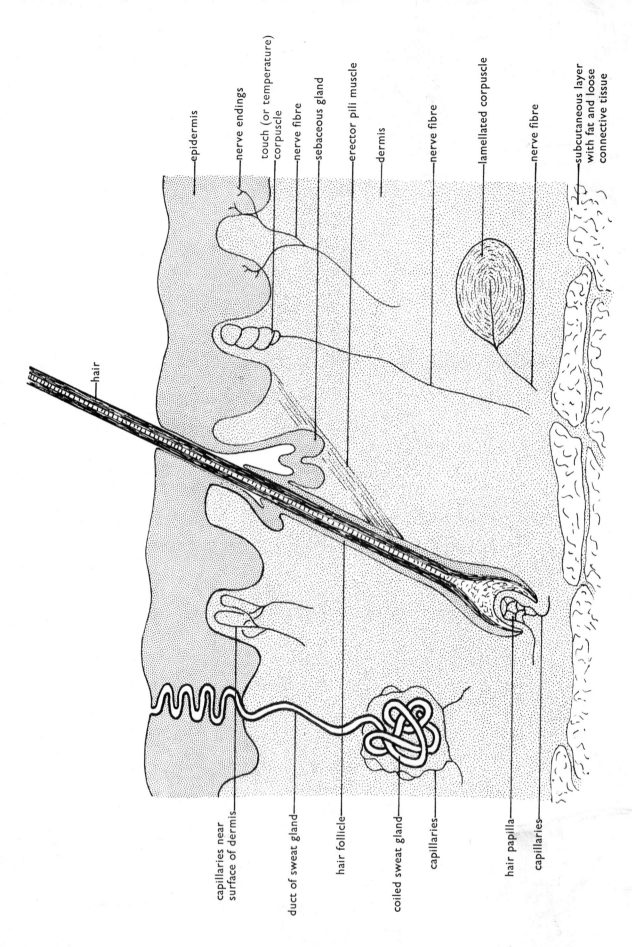

epidermis

nerve endings

touch (or temperature) corpuscle

nerve fibre

sebaceous gland

erector pili muscle

dermis

nerve fibre

lamellated corpuscle

nerve fibre

subcutaneous layer with fat and loose connective tissue

hair

capillaries near surface of dermis

duct of sweat gland

hair follicle

coiled sweat gland

capillaries

hair papilla

capillaries

Skin—*V.S.*

THE SKIN

The skin is formed of two layers of tissue, the **epidermis** and the **dermis.**

The EPIDERMIS consists of **stratified epithelium** in which the outer layers of cells are dead and cornified.

The DERMIS consists of dense **connective tissue** with nerves and blood vessels. Beneath it there is a subcutaneous layer of looser connective tissue with large fat deposits in adipose cells.

In the dermis but formed from the epidermis are **1. hair follicles, 2. sebaceous glands, 3. sweat glands.**

The Functions of the various parts of the Skin

1. The **cornified layer of the epidermis** protects the surface of the body against (i) friction, (ii) water loss, (iii) entry of germs. It is continuously renewed by growth of the germinative layer. Friction stimulates this growth of the germinative layer so that the epidermis becomes thicker where it has to withstand wear, e.g. on the soles of the feet. Nails are especially thick regions of epidermis on the tips of the fingers and toes.

2. The **dermis** connects the epidermis to the underlying structures. The fat in it gives insulation against heat loss and serves to a lesser extent as storage and padding.

3. The **hairs** in most mammals also give insulation by entangling pockets of air, but in man they are too sparse and short over most of the body to be of much use. The small erector muscle which is attached to each hair is a vestigial structure retained from the time when there was a complete hairy coat and the hairs could be made to stand on end with cold, fear or anger, thus deepening the layer of air and making the animal look larger.

4. The **sebaceous glands** produce an oily secretion called sebum which prevents the horny layer of the epidermis and the hairs from becoming brittle. The mammary glands which form milk after childbirth (see page 117), and the ceruminous glands which form wax in the outer ear passages, are specialised sebaceous glands.

5. The **sweat glands** produce a watery secretion containing salts and waste nitrogenous materials and are therefore excretory organs, but their chief function is to help to regulate body temperature. If the temperature tends to rise owing to heat liberated by muscular activity or to external conditions, the blood capillaries of the skin dilate so that more blood circulates near the surface of the body to be cooled. At the same time the sweat glands are active and the water of the sweat, by requiring heat to evaporate it, increases the cooling effect. Conversely, if the body temperature tends to fall, the skin capillaries contract and the sweat glands cease to function. The average normal body temperature, taken under the tongue, is 37 °C. Deep-seated, active organs have somewhat higher temperatures but the difference is kept minimal by the continual circulation of the blood (see page 91).

6. The **sensory nerve endings** of the skin perceive touch and temperature changes.

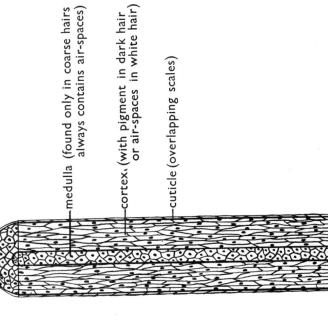

stratum corneum
stratum lucidum
stratum granulosum } zona cornea
stratum germinativum—zona germinativa

dead horny cells
granular cells
prickle cells
basal cells

Detail of structure of epidermis

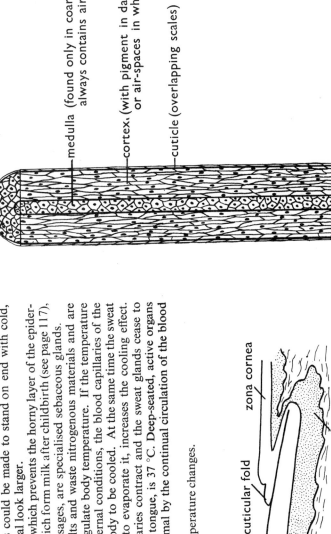

bundle of white fibres
ground substance
yellow elastic fibres
adipose cell distended with fat

fibroblast

young adipose cell

Connective tissue from dermis and subcutaneous layer

medulla (found only in coarse hairs always contains air-spaces)
cortex (with pigment in dark hair or air-spaces in white hair)
cuticle (overlapping scales)

Part of a hair

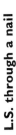

free border
nail
cuticular fold
zona cornea
nail bed
epidermis
zona germinativa
dermis

L.S. through a nail

THE TRUNK

The trunk has a framework of bone, cartilage and muscle surrounding two cavities within which lie the viscera. The cavities are separated from one another by a muscular partition called the diaphragm. The upper cavity with its walls constitutes the **thorax** and the lower cavity with its walls is the **abdomen.**

THE THORAX

The walls of the thorax are formed by the thoracic vertebrae, sternum, ribs and costal cartilages and the intercostal muscles. The floor of the thorax is formed by the diaphragm.

The **thoracic cavity** is conical in shape and contains:
1. the heart and roots of the great blood-vessels,
2. the lungs, bronchi and part of the trachea,
3. part of the oesophagus.
4. the thoracic duct,
5. parts of the sympathetic cords and vagus nerves.

THE ABDOMEN

The walls of the abdomen are formed by the lumbar vertebrae, parts of the lower ribs, the abdominal muscles and the pelvis. The roof of the abdomen is formed by the diaphragm.

The **abdominal cavity** is ovoid and its lower end opens into the **pelvic cavity,** which lies below the brim of the true pelvis and has the levator ani muscle for its floor. For convenience in describing the location of the abdominal viscera the abdomen is divided by four imaginary lines into nine regions.

The **abdominal cavity** contains:
1. the stomach, small intestine and large intestine except part of the pelvic colon and the rectum,
2. the liver and pancreas,
3. the spleen,
4. the kidneys and the greater part of each ureter,
5. the abdominal aorta and the greater part of the inferior vena cava,
6. the lower parts of the sympathetic cords.

The **pelvic cavity** contains:
1. part of the pelvic colon and the rectum,
2. the lower ends of the ureters, the bladder and the urethra,
3. the ovaries, Fallopian tubes, uterus and vagina of the female and the vasa efferentia and seminal vesicles of the male.

Note. During pregnancy the uterus rises into the abdominal cavity.

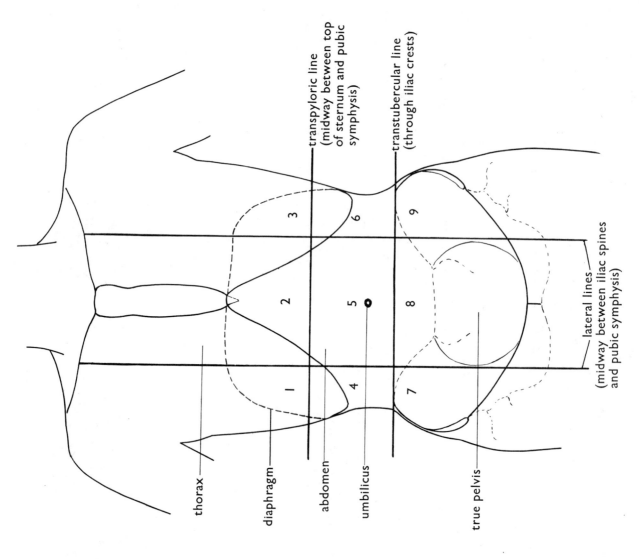

Regions of the abdomen

1 and 3 Hypochondriac regions
2 Epigastric region
4 and 6 Lumbar regions
5 Umbilical region
7 and 9 Iliac regions
8 Hypogastric region

Trunk

transpyloric line (midway between top of sternum and pubic symphysis)

transtubercular line (through iliac crests)

lateral lines (midway between iliac spines and pubic symphysis)

thorax

diaphragm

abdomen

umbilicus

true pelvis

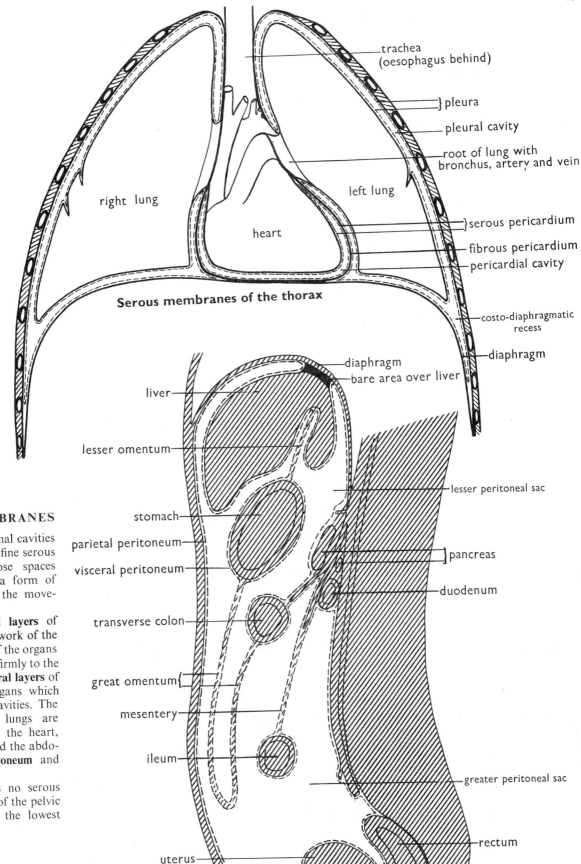

Serous membranes of the thorax

trachea
(oesophagus behind)

} pleura

pleural cavity

root of lung with
bronchus, artery and vein

} serous pericardium

fibrous pericardium

pericardial cavity

costo-diaphragmatic
recess

diaphragm

right lung

left lung

heart

diaphragm
bare area over liver

liver

lesser omentum

lesser peritoneal sac

stomach

parietal peritoneum

pancreas

visceral peritoneum

duodenum

transverse colon

great omentum

mesentery

ileum

greater peritoneal sac

uterus

rectum

peritoneum over
pelvic viscera

bladder

Serous membranes of the abdomen

THE SEROUS MEMBRANES

The thoracic and abdominal cavities are lined completely with fine serous membranes which enclose spaces filled with **serous fluid**, a form of lymph, which lubricates the movements of the viscera.

The outer or **parietal layers** of membrane line the framework of the cavities and cover some of the organs so that they are attached firmly to the walls. The inner or **visceral layers** of membrane cover the organs which are slung freely in the cavities. The membranes round the lungs are called the **pleura**, round the heart, the **pericardium** and round the abdominal viscera, the **peritoneum** and **mesenteries**.

The pelvic cavity has no serous spaces. The upper parts of the pelvic viscera are covered by the lowest part of the peritoneum.

THE DIGESTIVE SYSTEM

The digestive system consists of the alimentary canal and its associate glands and is concerned with the process of nutrition.

The process of nutrition involves:

1. **Ingestion** of the food through the mouth,
2. **Digestion** by which the food is broken down into a form suitable for
3. **Absorption** into the body, and
4. **Assimilation** by which it is used by the tissues.

DIGESTION

Digestion takes place in the alimentary canal. **Mechanical digestion** is the breakdown of the solid food into small pieces by the chewing action of the teeth and the churning action of the stomach wall. **Chemical digestion** is the breakdown of large molecules into smaller ones by hydrolysis, i.e. chemical breakdown using water to satisfy the broken bonds. Thus proteins which are long chain polypeptides are split into shorter chain polypeptides known as proteoses and peptones, and finally into their constituent amino-acids; fats are split into fatty acids and glycerol; and starches are split into disaccharides and finally into monosaccharides. These chemical changes are brought about by digestive enzymes, each of which is highly specific in its action and very sensitive to conditions, especially pH. (For table of digestive enzymes see page 85.)

Note. There are many enzymes in the body besides those of the digestive juices. All of them have their optimum activity at about body temperature and are destroyed by greater heat.

THE ALIMENTARY CANAL

Digestion and absorption take place during the passage of the food through the alimentary canal. This is a continuous tube, about 9 m long, from the mouth to the anus. Most of its length is coiled up in the abdominal cavity.

The alimentary canal is divided into the following regions:

1. Buccal cavity.
2. Pharynx.
3. Oesophagus.
4. Stomach.
5. Small intestine consisting of duodenum, jejunum and ileum.
6. Large intestine, consisting of caecum and appendix, colon and rectum.

THE BUCCAL CAVITY

The buccal cavity has the palate for its roof, the tongue on its floor, the cheeks for its sides and the lips in front. It is supported by the jaws, in which the teeth are set in sockets (see pages 7 and 10).

In the buccal cavity the food is chewed by the teeth, turned over and tasted by the tongue and mixed with saliva from the salivary glands (see page 82). The food mass or bolus is then swallowed.

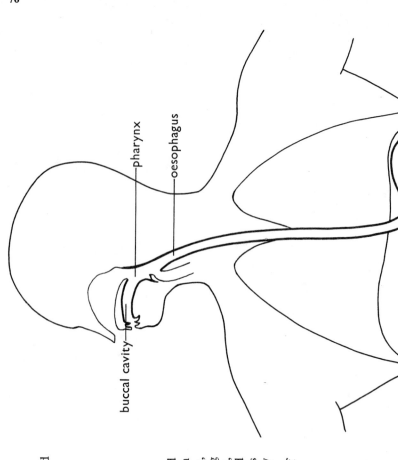

pharynx

oesophagus

buccal cavity

stomach

pancreatic-duct

transverse colon

descending colon

pelvic colon

rectum

anal canal

gall bladder

bile-duct

duodenum

jejunum

ileum

ascending colon

caecum

appendix

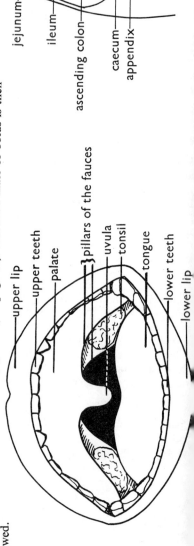

upper lip

upper teeth

palate

}pillars of the fauces

uvula

tonsil

tongue

lower teeth

lower lip

The pharynx is divided into the **naso-pharynx** at the back of the nose and the **oro-pharynx** at the back of the mouth. During swallowing these two regions are separated by the soft palate and the opening from the pharynx into the larynx is closed by the raising and pulling of the larynx forwards. At the same time the epiglottis lies back over the glottis.

The **tonsils** are special large patches of lymph tissue which lie at the side of the pharynx between the **pillars of the fauces.**

The rest of the alimentary canal is a simple tube whose walls are made up of four coats:

1. an outer **fibrous** or **serous coat,**
2. a **muscular coat** for the most part made of smooth muscle with the outer layers of fibres longitudinal and the inner layers circular,
3. **submucosa** of connective tissue with many blood-vessels,
4. **mucosa** consisting chiefly of connective tissue with blood-vessels but separated from the submucosa by the muscle layer called the **muscularis mucosae** and having epithelium for its surface layer.

THE OESOPHAGUS

The oesophagus is a straight tube through the neck and thorax close behind the trachea but in front of the descending part of the aorta. Its distinguishing features are:

1. stratified epithelium for the mucous membrane,
2. numerous longitudinal folds which allow stretching,
3. relatively thick muscularis mucosae,
4. striated muscles for the upper two-thirds of its length.

Food is passed rapidly through the oesophagus by **peristalsis**, i.e. regular waves of muscular movement.

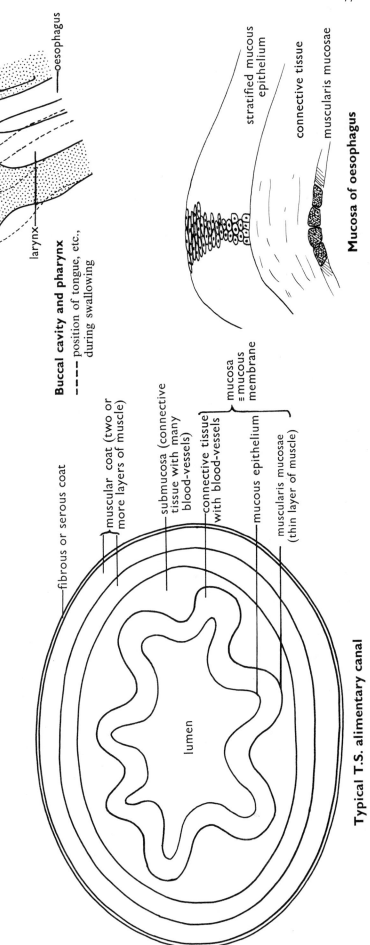

Buccal cavity and pharynx
- - - position of tongue, etc., during swallowing

Mucosa of oesophagus

Typical T.S. alimentary canal

The Stomach

The stomach lies close below the diaphragm to the left of the liver. It is suspended by its mesentery, a fold of which hangs down as the greater omentum (see page 75). Its shape varies with the amount of food in it. The opening into the stomach is guarded by the **cardiac sphincter,** and the opening to the duodenum, by the **pyloric sphincter.**

The wall of the stomach is characterised by:
1. a layer of oblique muscle fibres in addition to the circular and longitudinal ones,
2. temporary folds of the mucosa called rugae,
3. numerous tubular gastric glands.

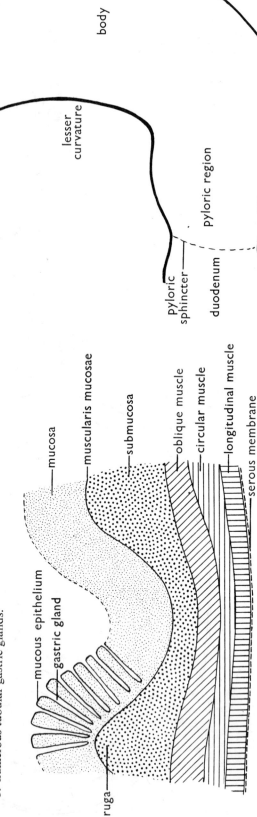

Diagrammatic section through the wall of stomach

The functions of the stomach are:
1. churning of the food to break up large particles and mix them with the gastric juice;
2. secretion, by the cardiac and pyloric glands and the neck cells of the fundus glands, of **mucus** which lubricates the passage of food;
3. secretion by the fundus and body glands of **gastric juice** containing:
   (a) **hydrochloric acid,** from the oxyntic or parietal cells, which stops the action of salivary amylase, allows pepsin to work and curdles milk;
   (b) **pepsin** (secreted as pepsinogen) which attacks the bonds between certain amino acids in proteins, thus producing proteoses and peptones;
4. secretion of the hormone, **gastrin,** which stimulates the gastric glands to activity when food containing substances called **secretagogues** is in the stomach;
5. absorption of alcohol.

The final product that leaves the stomach when the pyloric sphincter relaxes is called **chyme.**

Note. Rennin is present in the gastric juice of many young mammals, but it is doubtful if it is ever produced in

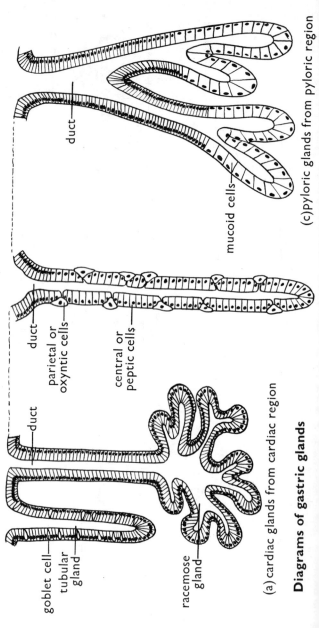

Diagrams of gastric glands

(a) cardiac glands from cardiac region

(c) pyloric glands from pyloric region

...denum, which curves around the pancreas and into which the **pancreatic duct** and the **bile duct** open. The rest of the small intestine forms the **jejunum** (about 2·5 m) and the **ileum** (about 4·2 m). The duodenum lies against the back wall of the abdomen, but the jejunum and ileum are suspended by **mesentery** (see page 75).

The wall of the small intestine is relatively thin. It is characterised by:

1. circular folds of the mucosa which decrease and disappear in the ileum;

2. lymph nodules which increase in numbers and become aggregated into **Peyer's patches** in the ileum;

3. numerous tubular glands called **crypts of Lieberkuhn**, the walls of which have many **goblet cells** and undifferentiated cells in a state of active division;

4. small, rounded **Brunner's glands** opening into the bases of the crypts of Lieberkuhn in the duodenum only;

5. **villi**, each containing a lymph vessel called a **lacteal** and a group of **blood capillaries** (see overleaf) and covered with goblet cells and absorptive cells with striated borders, which have a life of only 1–2 days before they break up and are replaced by cells migrating from the crypts of Lieberkuhn.

stomach

jejunum

duodenum

pyloric sphincter

bile-duct

pancreatic-duct

openings of bile- and pancreatic- ducts on papilla

Duodenum

striated border

columnar epithelial cell

goblet cell

Epithelium of villus

The functions of the small intestine are:

1. **Peristaltic**, **antiperistaltic**, and **occlusive movements** mix the food with (a) **bile** (see page 84), (b) **pancreatic juice** (see page 83), and (c) **intestinal juice**. These movements also bring the digested food into contact with the absorptive surfaces of the villi.

2. **Intestinal juice** is produced, chiefly by the glands of the duodenum, but with contributions from shed epithelial cells and intestinal bacteria and mucus from the goblet cells. Intestinal juice contains a mixture of enzymes:

(a) **maltase, sucrase**, and **lactase**, which split the corresponding disaccharides into their constituent monosaccharides,

(b) **enterokinase** which activates trypsinogen of the pancreatic juice (see page 83),

(c) **peptidases** which split medium and short chain polypeptides into amino acids (see table on page 85).

3. Digested food is **absorbed** through the walls of the villi. Neutral fats, fatty acids, and glycerol pass into the lymph vessels where they cause the 'milky' appearance which gives these vessels the name lacteals. The 'milky' lymph is called **chyle**. Amino acids and sugars pass directly to the liver via the portal vein.

4. Three hormones are known to be secreted by the small intestine. **Secretin** and **pancreozymin** stimulate production of pancreatic juice while **enterocrinin** governs secretion of the intestinal juice.

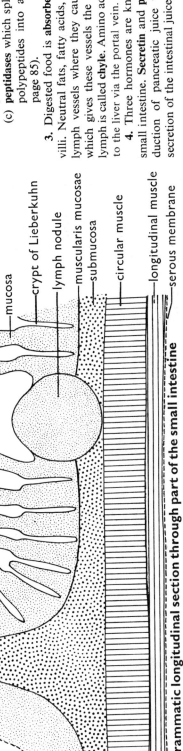

circular fold

villus

mucosa

crypt of Lieberkuhn

lymph nodule

muscularis mucosae

submucosa

circular muscle

longitudinal muscle

serous membrane

Diagrammatic longitudinal section through part of the small intestine

The Large Intestine

The large intestine is about 1·5 m long and is formed of the caecum with the appendix, the colon and the rectum. It is coiled around the small intestine and only the transverse colon and a small part of the pelvic colon hang freely suspended by mesentery, the rest being more closely attached to the abdominal wall.

The **caecum** is a small pouch to which the appendix is attached and into which the ileum opens through the ileo-caecal or ileo-colic valve.

The **colon** is sacculated and has three distinct bends or flexures.

The **rectum** is only about 120 mm long and runs directly through the pelvis, to the anal canal. The latter has a sphincter of voluntary (striated) muscle by which defaecation is controlled.

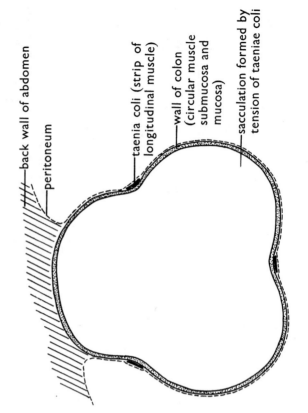

T.S. colon showing taeniae coli and peritoneum

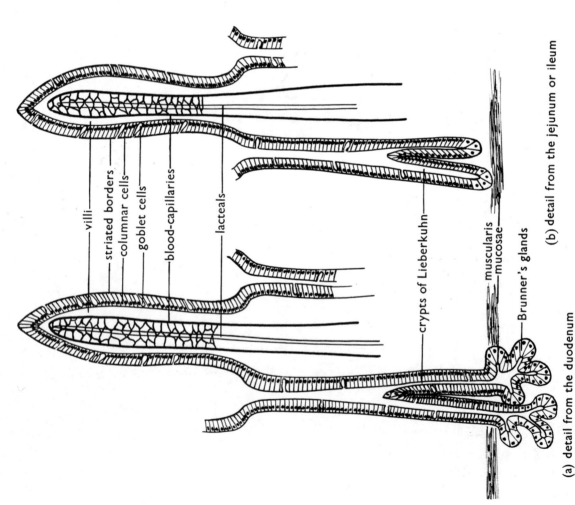

(a) detail from the duodenum

(b) detail from the jejunum or ileum

Diagram of glands and villi of the intestine

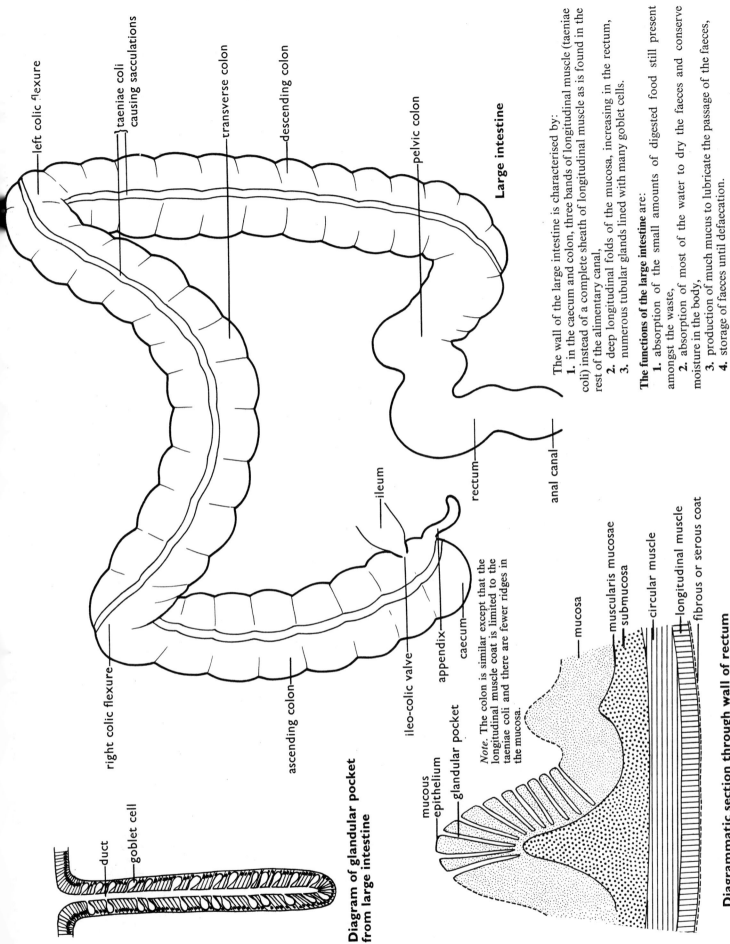

left colic flexure

taeniae coli
causing sacculations

transverse colon

descending colon

pelvic colon

Large intestine

right colic flexure

ascending colon

ileum

ileo-colic valve

appendix

caecum

rectum

anal canal

**Diagram of glandular pocket
from large intestine**

duct

goblet cell

mucous
epithelium

glandular pocket

Note. The colon is similar except that the longitudinal muscle coat is limited to the taeniae coli and there are fewer ridges in the mucosa.

mucosa

muscularis mucosae

submucosa

circular muscle

longitudinal muscle

fibrous or serous coat

Diagrammatic section through wall of rectum

The wall of the large intestine is characterised by:
1. in the caecum and colon, three bands of longitudinal muscle (taeniae coli) instead of a complete sheath of longitudinal muscle as is found in the rest of the alimentary canal,
2. deep longitudinal folds of the mucosa, increasing in the rectum,
3. numerous tubular glands lined with many goblet cells.

The functions of the large intestine are:
1. absorption of the small amounts of digested food still present amongst the waste,
2. absorption of most of the water to dry the faeces and conserve moisture in the body,
3. production of much mucus to lubricate the passage of the faeces,
4. storage of faeces until defaecation.

The Glands associated with the Alimentary Canal

Glands are single cells, groups of cells or organs which produce secretions. In the digestive system there are:

1. Unicellular glands, the goblet cells, which secrete mucus.
2. Multicellular glands which may be simple or compound.

The gastric glands and duodenal glands are simple tubular glands, which produce gastric juice and intestinal juice respectively (see pages 78 and 79).

The salivary glands, pancreas and liver are compound or racemose glands.

THE SALIVARY GLANDS

There are three pairs of large compound salivary glands as well as numerous small isolated salivary glands on the lips, cheeks and tongue. The ducts of these glands open into the buccal cavity.

Each salivary gland is composed of secretory alveoli and their ductules. A group of alveoli constitutes an acinus and in the large glands many acini are bound by connective tissue into lobules, the lobules themselves being bound into lobes.

The Functions of the Salivary Glands

The salivary glands produce **saliva**, which is a mixture of mucus from the mucous-secreting cells with a watery secretion containing salts and the enzyme, **salivary amylase**, from the serous cells. Water moistens and softens the food, mucus makes it slippery to ease swallowing, the salts prevent excessive acidity occurring in the mouth so that salivary amylase can do its work of beginning the digestion of cooked starch into dextrin and maltose.

The salivary glands may also excrete both organic and inorganic substances, e.g. lead in cases of lead poisoning.

Salivary glands

Pancreas in duodenal loop

parotid gland (in front of ear, below zygomatic arch and over angle of mandible)

zygomatic arch

sublingual gland (under tongue)

submandibular gland (under mandible)

tongue

sublingual fold

parotid duct (opening opposite 2nd upper molar)

c. 12 sublingual ducts (opening on sublingual fold under the side of the tongue)

submandibular or Wharton's duct (opening on frenulum under front of tongue)

duct

mucous cells (secrete mucus)

(1) sublingual, labial, buccal and palatine glands (secrete mucus only)

duct

serous cells (secrete salivary amylase)

crescent of Gianuzzi

mucous cells (secrete mucus)

(2) submandibular and anterior lingual glands (secrete mucus and salivary amylase)

(3) parotid glands and glands of vallate papillae of tongue (secrete salivary amylase only)

Sections of parts of various salivary glands

pylorus

tail of pancreas

body of pancreas

jejunum

uncinate process of pancreas

notch for mesenteric artery and vein

head of pancreas

duodenum

bile-duct

accessory pancreatic-duct

pancreatic-duct

duodenal papilla with openings of bile- and pancreatic-ducts

The pancreas lies in the loop of the duodenum and behind the stomach.

Like the salivary glands, the pancreas is composed of numerous lobules each containing secretory alveoli but, in addition, between groups of these alveoli, there are the islets of Langerhans which are masses of cells unconnected to ducts.

The Functions of the Pancreas

The alveoli secrete pancreatic juice containing water, alkaline salts, the enzymes **lipase** and **pancreatic amylase** and the enzyme precursors **trypsinogen** and **chymotrypsinogen.** The alkalinity of pancreatic juice helps to neutralise the acidity of chyme from the stomach and so allows the pancreatic and intestinal enzymes to work. Lipase splits fats into fatty acids and glycerol. Pancreatic amylase splits starch, cooked or uncooked, and dextrin into maltose. Enterokinase in the intestine converts trypsinogen into trypsin. Trypsin then converts chymotrypsinogen into chymotrypsin. The two active enzymes, trypsin and chymotrypsin, then attack different bonds in the proteins from those attacked by pepsin. Small quantities of amino acids are liberated, but the main residues are still polypeptides until acted on by the peptidases of the intestinal juice (see page 79).

The **islets of Langerhans** are endocrine glands that secrete two hormones, **insulin** and **glucagon.** Insulin lowers the level of sugar in the blood by helping the general body cells to take it up and use it or store it as glycogen. Glucagon raises the level of sugar in the blood by stimulating the breakdown of liver glycogen. Thus together they help to transfer blood to the general body tissues and to maintain a constant level of sugar in the blood. The action of glucagon is similar to that of epinephrine (see page 109), but insulin has no counterpart. Lack of insulin deprives the tissues of nourishment and causes diabetes melitus.

islet of Langerhans

duct

alveolus (gland cells active)

alveolus (gland cells inactive)

Sections of pancreas

THE LIVER

The liver lies below the diaphragm to the right of, and overlapping, the stomach. It is held in place by the falciform (sickle-shaped) ligament, the right and left lateral ligaments and the round ligament. The round ligament is formed from the umbilical vein (see page 115).

The liver weighs about 1·3 kg and is the largest gland in the body, having large right and left lobes and small caudate and quadrate lobes.

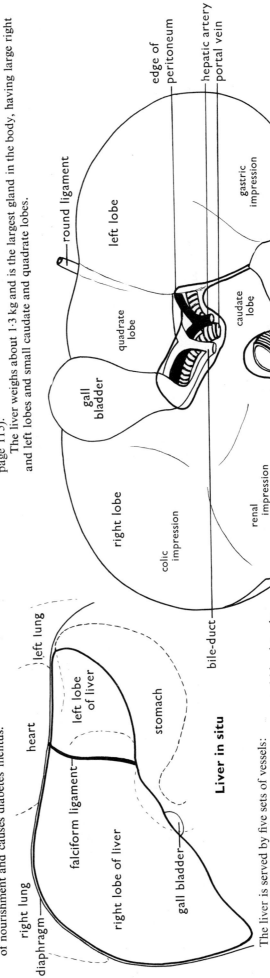

round ligament — edge of peritoneum — hepatic artery — portal vein — left lobe — quadrate lobe — gall bladder — caudate lobe — gastric impression — inferior vena cava — supra-renal impression — renal impression — colic impression — right lobe — bile-duct

Liver viewed from beneath

right lung — diaphragm — heart — left lung — falciform ligament — left lobe of liver — right lobe of liver — gall bladder — stomach

Liver in situ

The liver is served by five sets of vessels:

1. the **hepatic artery** which brings oxygenated blood to the liver tissue.

2. the **portal vein** which brings large amounts of food from the alimentary canal and iron from the spleen,

3. the **hepatic veins** which take the blood away from the liver to the inferior vena cava,

4. the **lymphatics** which remove the little lymph that is formed,

5. the **bile ducts** which carry away bile secreted into them from the liver cells.

The Structure of the Liver

The liver appears to be made up of many tiny lobules which are polygonal in transverse section and thimble-shaped in vertical section. Each lobule is surrounded by a connective tissue sheath called a Glisson's capsule. Inside each lobule the liver cells are arranged in radiating rows called liver cords between which blood flows in channels known as the sinusoids. The functional units of the liver centre on the strands of connective tissue known as the portal canals in which lie the bile ducts and branches of the hepatic artery and of the portal vein.

liver cords (radiating from centre of lobule)

intralobular vein

arteriole
bile-duct
interlobular vein

Glisson's capsule

artery, vein, bile-duct in portal canal

T.S. Liver

The Functions of the Liver

The liver has many functions the most important of which may be classified into three groups: **1.** secretory, **2.** storage, and **3.** metabolic.

1. THE SECRETORY FUNCTIONS include the production of bile and of heparin.

(a) **Bile** is concentrated and temporarily stored in the gall bladder. It is slightly alkaline, so that it helps to neutralise the acidity of chyme from the stomach; and it consists of a solution of bile salts and bile pigments. Bile salts emulsify fats in the small intestine and assist absorption of fatty acids and of neutral fats in finely emulsified form. Bile pigments, bilirubin and biliverdin, are waste materials formed by the Kupffer cells from the remains of red blood-corpuscles (erythrocytes) which have been partially destroyed in the spleen. They are partially reabsorbed in the small intestine and re-excreted in the urine. The residue colours the faeces and is removed with them through the anus.

(b) **Heparin** is an internal secretion which helps to prevent the clotting of blood in the circulation. It is formed by other tissues also (see pages 90 and 91).

2. THE STORAGE FUNCTIONS include the storage of vitamins A, B and D, iron and glycogen.

(a) **Vitamins A, B, and D** are stored until required. Vitamin B_{12} is identical with the anti-anaemic or erythrocyte maturation factor of the liver and is essential for the formation of new red blood-cells.

(b) **Iron** comes from the breakdown of worn-out red blood-corpuscles. It is stored until required for the manufacture of the haemoglobin for new red blood-corpuscles.

(c) **Glycogen** is formed from glucose in the presence of specific enzymes in the liver cells but the reaction is reversible and whether glycogen is formed or glucose liberated depends on the amount of sugar in the blood and the hormonal balance including the effects of insulin, glucagon, and **adrenaline**.

3. THE METABOLIC FUNCTIONS include conversions and syntheses involving fats, proteins and carbohydrates, and also detoxication processes.

(a) Many **fats** taken in during feeding are unsuitable for assimilation and have to be **desaturated** before they can be used. Fatty acid oxidation breaks down the higher fatty acids so that the products can be stored and used by other tissues.

(b) Excess and unsuitable **amino-acids** are **deaminated** by the removal of the amino groups. The organic radicles or ketoacids are converted into carbohydrate and used as such. Some of the amino groups are stored and can be used to reaminate ketoacids but most of them are converted into **urea** to prevent the accumulation of free ammonia which is poisonous to the tissues.

(c) The breakdown of unwanted nucleo-proteins produces uric acid.

(d) All the proteins of the blood-plasma except globulin are synthesised in the liver.

(e) Any carbohydrate in excess of what can be stored as glycogen is converted into fat for storage elsewhere.

(f) Many drugs and other poisonous substances are destroyed or neutralised by the liver.

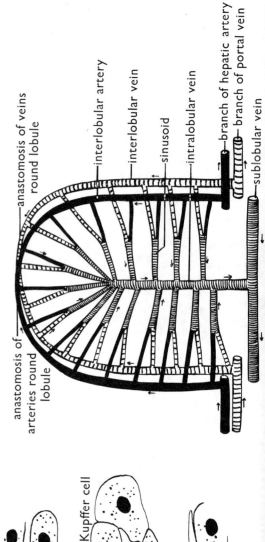

anastomosis of veins round lobule

interlobular artery

interlobular vein

sinusoid

intralobular vein

branch of hepatic artery
branch of portal vein

sublobular vein

anastomosis of arteries round lobule

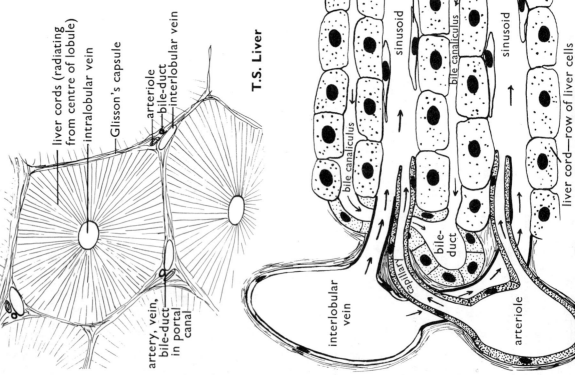

interlobular vein

Kupffer cell

sinusoid

bile canaliculus

bile canaliculus

bile-duct

capillary

sinusoid

liver cord—row of liver cells

arteriole

Diagram to show relationship of blood-

DIGESTIVE JUICES

Secretion	Where produced	Where effective	Principal components	Action of components
Saliva	Salivary glands	Mouth (and temporarily in stomach)	Water Mucus Salts SALIVARY AMYLASE	Softens food Makes food slippery Provide **neutral** medium for action of salivary amylase and help to preserve teeth against acids formed by bacteria Splits cooked **starch** into **dextrin** and **maltose**
Gastric juice	Gastric glands	Stomach	Water Mucus Hydrochloric acid PEPSIN (secreted as pepsinogen) RENNIN	Further softens food Prevents gastric juice from damaging the stomach wall Stops the action of salivary amylase and allows pepsin to work. Kills many germs. Curdles milk Splits certain **proteins** into **proteoses** and **peptones**, i.e. shorter chain polypeptides Curdles milk in adults (when rennin scarce or absent and in any case ineffective) Curdles milk in many young mammals. Presence in man doubtful
Bile	Liver (stored in the gall bladder)	Small intestine	Water Bile pigments Bile salts	Waste materials—excreted with faeces or absorbed and re-excreted later Alkaline therefore neutralise acidity of chyme and stop action of pepsin but allow action of intestinal enzymes. Emulsify fats
Pancreatic juice	Pancreas	Small intestine	Water Alkaline salts PANCREATIC LIPASE PANCREATIC AMYLASE TRYPSIN (secreted as trypsinogen) CHYMOTRYPSIN (secreted as chymotrypsinogen)	Help to increase alkalinity in intestine and combine with fatty acids to form soaps Splits fats into **fatty acids** and **glycerol** (Acts more effectively than gastric lipase as fat is emulsified) Splits all forms of **starch** and **dextrin** into **maltose** Split certain proteins, proteoses and peptones into shorter polypeptide chains and liberate some amino-acids
Intestinal juice	Duodenal glands and goblet cells throughout the small intestine	Small intestine	Water Mucus ENTEROKINASE PEPTIDASES Carboxypeptidase Aminopeptidase Dipeptidase MALTASE SUCRASE LACTASE	Protects intestinal mucosa Activates **trypsinogen** forming **trypsin**; trypsin then activates **chymotrysinogen** Split amino-acids, one at a time, from the acid and amino ends, respectively, of the polypeptide chains Splits the final dipeptide residues Splits **maltose** into **glucose** Splits **sucrose** into **glucose** and **fructose** Splits **lactose** into **glucose** and **galactose**

ASSIMILATION

Assimilation is the process whereby the food materials are used in the metabolism of the body.

Metabolic processes may be classified as:

1. **anabolic** or constructive processes whereby more complicated substances are made from simpler ones,

2. **katabolic** or destructive processes whereby complicated substances are broken down into waste materials, usually with the liberation of energy.

Carbohydrate metabolism. Most of the carbohydrate is absorbed as glucose. This can be stored in limited quantities as glycogen and is used for the liberation of energy (1 g yields 18 joules). In muscular action about 15% of the energy is in the form of muscular work. The other 85% is in the form of heat. Excess carbohydrate is converted into fat.

Fat metabolism. The fatty acids and glycerol recombine, after absorption, to form fats in the body. Fats can be stored in unlimited quantities, particularly in the skin and mesenteries, where they form insulation and padding, and are used for the liberation of energy chiefly as heat (1 g yields 39 joules).

Protein metabolism. The amino-acids absorbed are recombined to form the body proteins for the growth of new protoplasm and the repair of old. Excess and unwanted amino-acids are deaminated. The nitrogenous or amino part is largely converted into urea and excreted. The organic part or ketoacid is converted into carbohydrate and used as such for the liberation of energy (1 g yields 18 joules).

Carbohydrates, fats and proteins are also used for the construction of such complex substances as enzymes and hormones of which there are an unknown number of varieties.

Besides these organic substances, a good-balanced diet contains: **1. vitamins**, a number of special substances which cannot be made in the body but which are needed for a variety of purposes, e.g. the prevention of scurvy and rickets, the functioning of the respiratory oxidation and the formation of rhodopsin (see page 70), **2. a variety of inorganic salts** which are needed for a variety of purposes such as bone and tooth formation, blood-salts, construction of haemoglobin and thryoxine, **3. sufficient water** to replace inevitable losses and to wash away waste materials through the kidneys, **4.** sufficient indigestible **roughage** to stimulate the movements of the alimentary canal and thus prevent constipation.

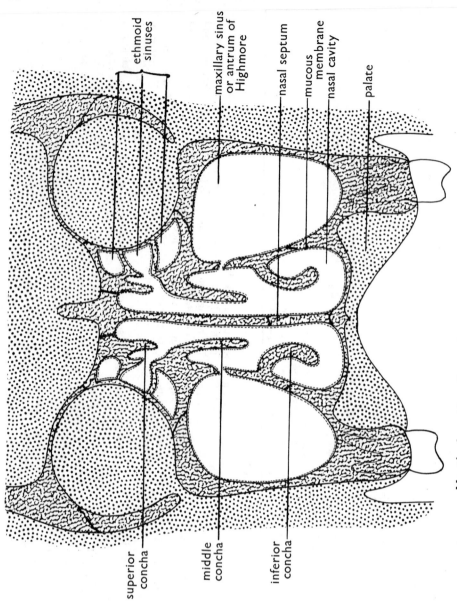

Labels (top): ethmoid sinuses; maxillary sinus or antrum of Highmore; nasal septum; mucous membrane; nasal cavity; palate

Labels (bottom): superior concha; middle concha; inferior concha

Vertical section through the nasal cavities and sinuses

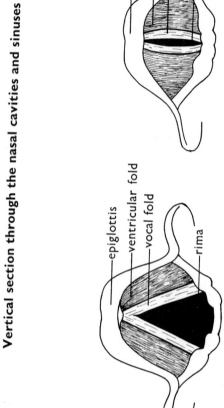

Labels: epiglottis; ventricular fold; vocal fold; rima

Vocal folds with rima of the glottis open, as when breathing quietly

Labels: epiglottis; ventricular fold; vocal fold; rima

Vocal folds with rima of the glottis closed, as when speaking

THE RESPIRATORY SYSTEM

RESPIRATION

Respiration is the process whereby oxygen is obtained and used for the oxidation of food materials to liberate energy and to produce carbon dioxide and water as waste materials.

INTERNAL or TISSUE RESPIRATION is the chain of chemical processes which take place in every living cell to free energy needed for its vital activities. A number of reactions, each with its own catalytic enzymes, are involved and the energy is liberated in small quantities at a number of different stages in the chain, but when carbohydrate is the raw material oxidised, the total effect is:

$$C_6H_{12}O_6 + 6O_2 = 6CO_2 + 6H_2O + energy$$

glucose + oxygen = carbon dioxide + water

In this case the respiratory quotient or $\dfrac{amount\ CO_2}{amount\ O_2} = 1$, but if fat is oxidised, relatively more oxygen is required and the respiratory quotient is about 0·7. The normal average respiratory quotient due to the oxidation of a mixture of food-substances is about 0·85.

EXTERNAL RESPIRATION is the means by which the oxygen is obtained and the carbon dioxide removed from the body. This exchange of gases takes place in the respiratory organs, the lungs. A supply of fresh air is brought to the respiratory surface through the respiratory passages by the respiratory movements or breathing and the gases are conveyed between the lungs and the tissues by the blood.

THE STRUCTURE OF THE RESPIRATORY SYSTEM

THE RESPIRATORY SYSTEM consists of the nasal passages, the pharynx (shared with the alimentary canal), the larynx, the trachea, the bronchi and the lungs.

THE NASAL PASSAGES are separated from one another by the nasal septum and are lined with ciliated mucous membrane whose surface is vastly increased by the conchae. The nasal mucosa is continuous with the linings of the frontal, ethmoid, sphenoid and maxillary sinuses. (See also page 10.)

Air passing through the nose is warmed to body temperature and saturated with moisture by contact with the warm, damp mucous membrane. Dust and germs in the air are filtered out partly by the hairs round the nostrils and partly by adhesion to the slimy mucus which is produced by glands in the mucosa. Cilia move this mucus gradually into the pharynx whence it is swallowed. Slightly salty exudation from the mucosa and lacrimal secretion from the eyes (see page 69) have a mild disinfectant action. Smells in the air are detected by olfactory nerve endings in the mucosa of the upper parts of the nasal cavities (see

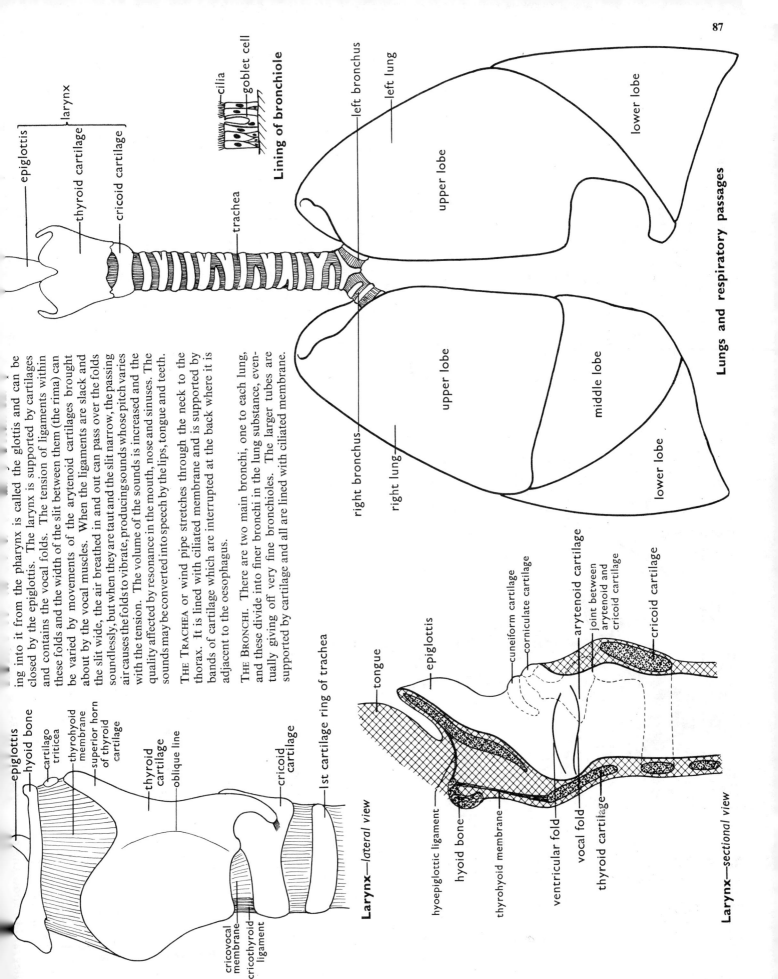

larynx
{ epiglottis
thyroid cartilage
cricoid cartilage

cilia
goblet cell

Lining of bronchiole

trachea

left bronchus
left lung

upper lobe

lower lobe

right bronchus
right lung

upper lobe

middle lobe

lower lobe

Lungs and respiratory passages

ing into it from the pharynx is called the glottis and can be closed by the epiglottis. The larynx is supported by cartilages and contains the vocal folds. The tension of ligaments within these folds and the width of the slit between them (the rima) can be varied by movements of the arytenoid cartilages brought about by the vocal muscles. When the ligaments are slack and the slit wide, the air breathed in and out can pass over the folds soundlessly, but when they are taut and the slit narrow, the passing air causes the folds to vibrate, producing sounds whose pitch varies with the tension. The volume of the sounds is increased and the quality affected by resonance in the mouth, nose and sinuses. The sounds may be converted into speech by the lips, tongue and teeth.

THE TRACHEA or wind pipe stretches through the neck to the thorax. It is lined with ciliated membrane and is supported by bands of cartilage which are interrupted at the back where it is adjacent to the oesophagus.

THE BRONCHI. There are two main bronchi, one to each lung, and these divide into finer bronchi in the lung substance, eventually giving off very fine bronchioles. The larger tubes are supported by cartilage and all are lined with ciliated membrane.

epiglottis
hyoid bone
cartilago triticea
thyrohyoid membrane
superior horn of thyroid cartilage
thyroid cartilage
oblique line
cricoid cartilage
1st cartilage ring of trachea
cricovocal membrane
cricothyroid ligament

Larynx—*lateral view*

tongue
epiglottis
cuneiform cartilage
corniculate cartilage
arytenoid cartilage
joint between arytenoid and cricoid cartilage
cricoid cartilage
hyoepiglottic ligament
hyoid bone
thyrohyoid membrane
ventricular fold
vocal fold
thyroid cartilage

Larynx—*sectional view*

The Method of Functioning of the Lungs

Oxygen from the air in the lungs dissolves in the thin film of moisture on the cells lining the alveoli, and then diffuses through these cells and through the walls of the capillaries into the plasma of the blood. From the plasma it diffuses into the red blood corpuscles and combines with haemoglobin to form oxyhaemoglobin. In this way the blood can carry about seventy times more oxygen than would be possible in simple solution.

In the other tissues of the body the utilisation of oxygen produces an oxygen gradient in the opposite direction. The oxyhaemoglobin breaks down and oxygen diffuses out of the blood, while carbonic acid from dissolved carbon dioxide diffuses in. Carbonic acid is carried in the blood as bicarbonate in the plasma and corpuscles and also in combination with haemoglobin as carbaminohaemoglobin.

When blood returns to the lungs, the carbaminohaemoglobin and some of the bicarbonate break down to liberate carbonic acid, which in turn liberates carbon dioxide in conditions of low carbon dioxide concentration. If the carbon dioxide concentration in the lungs rises, it interferes with this breakdown, and the consequent slight increase in acidity of the blood (decrease in pH) stimulates the respiratory centres of the brain to increase the breathing movements.

Breathing

Though breathing can, to a certain extent, be controlled voluntarily, it is normally a reflex action whose rate varies with body activity, i.e. with carbon dioxide production.

INSPIRATION, or breathing in, is brought about by (*a*) contraction of the diaphragm, which increases the depth of the thorax, and (*b*) contraction of the intercostal muscles which swing the ribs outwards and upwards and thus increase the diameter of the thorax. Both movements combine to increase the capacity of the thorax and thus suck air into the lungs through the respiratory passages. The air drawn in mixes with the air already present; therefore the air in the lungs always contains less oxygen and more carbon dioxide than the air actually drawn in.

EXPIRATION, or breathing out, is brought about by elastic recoil when the muscles relax.

Normally about 1 pint of air (tidal air) is changed at each breath, but additional air can be inspired (complemental air), and more air can be forced out (supplemental air), by the use of the pectoral and abdominal muscles in addition to the normal muscles of respiration.

Note. For a more detailed description of the breathing movements see page 52.

Average composition of air:

(a) Inspired		(b) Expired	
Nitrogen	78%	Nitrogen	78%
Inert gases	1%	Inert gases	1%
Oxygen	21%	Oxygen	17%
Carbon dioxide—negligible		Carbon dioxide	4%
Water vapour—variable		Water vapour—to saturation	

THE LUNGS lie in the thorax, invested in serous membranes called pleura and separated from one another by the mediastinum, in which lie the heart and the great blood-vessels (see page 75).

The right lung has three lobes and the left lung two lobes. Each lobe is made up of numerous lobules bound together by loose connective tissue. Each lobule consists of a group of air chambers attached to a terminal bronchiole. The air chambers are lined throughout with pavement epithelium. Close to this epithelium is a dense network of very fine blood capillaries which link the pulmonary arteries to the pulmonary veins.

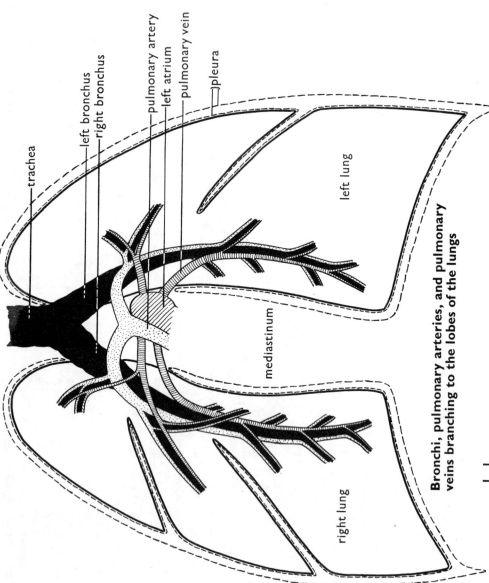

Bronchi, pulmonary arteries, and pulmonary veins branching to the lobes of the lungs

complemental air—c 1500 mls (can be drawn in by forced inspiration)

tidal air—c 500 mls (normal breath)

supplemental air—c 1500 mls (can be forced out by forced expiration)

residual air—c 1000 mls (left after forced expiration)

vital capacity

reserve air

Note. 500 mls.—approx. 1 pint

Diagram to show the capacity of the lungs

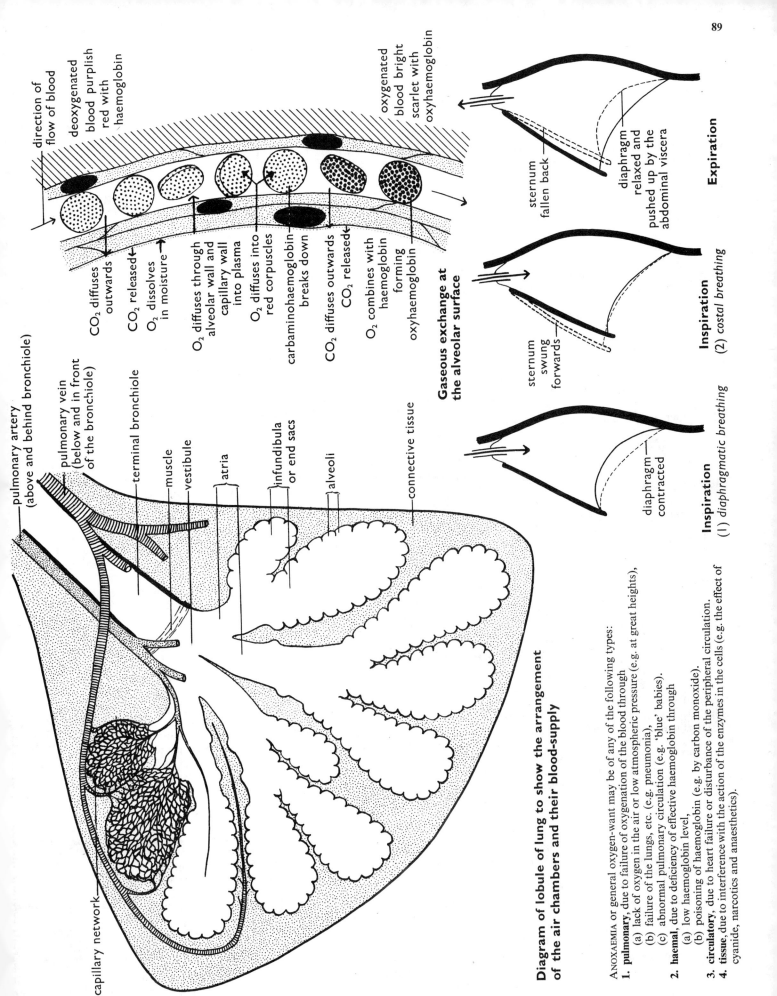

direction of flow of blood

deoxygenated blood purplish red with haemoglobin

oxygenated blood bright scarlet with oxyhaemoglobin

CO_2 diffuses outwards

CO_2 released

O_2 dissolves in moisture

O_2 diffuses through alveolar wall and capillary wall into plasma

O_2 diffuses into red corpuscles

carbaminohaemoglobin breaks down

CO_2 diffuses outwards CO_2 released

O_2 combines with haemoglobin forming oxyhaemoglobin

Gaseous exchange at the alveolar surface

sternum fallen back

diaphragm relaxed and pushed up by the abdominal viscera

Expiration

sternum swung forwards

Inspiration
(2) *costal breathing*

diaphragm contracted

Inspiration
(1) *diaphragmatic breathing*

pulmonary artery (above and behind bronchiole)

pulmonary vein (below and in front of the bronchiole)

terminal bronchiole

muscle

vestibule

atria

infundibula or end sacs

alveoli

connective tissue

capillary network

Diagram of lobule of lung to show the arrangement of the air chambers and their blood-supply

ANOXAEMIA or general oxygen-want may be of any of the following types:
1. **pulmonary**, due to failure of oxygenation of the blood through
    (a) lack of oxygen in the air or low atmospheric pressure (e.g. at great heights),
    (b) failure of the lungs, etc. (e.g. pneumonia),
    (c) abnormal pulmonary circulation (e.g. 'blue' babies).
2. **haemal**, due to deficiency of effective haemoglobin through
    (a) low haemoglobin level,
    (b) poisoning of haemoglobin (e.g. by carbon monoxide).
3. **circulatory**, due to heart failure or disturbance of the peripheral circulation.
4. **tissue**, due to interference with the action of the enzymes in the cells (e.g. the effect of cyanide, narcotics and anaesthetics).

THE BLOOD VASCULAR SYSTEM

BLOOD is a fluid tissue contained within a closed system of vessels, the **arteries**, **veins** and **capillaries**, through which it is made to circulate by the pumping action of the **heart**. It is the chief transport system of the body.

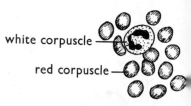

white corpuscle

red corpuscle

BLOOD

Blood forms about 7–9% of the total body weight in man. It appears to the naked eye as a viscous red fluid but when examined more carefully is found to consist of a yellow liquid portion called **plasma** and large numbers of cells called **corpuscles**. About 55% of the total volume of blood is plasma and the other 45% corpuscles.

Blood smear

PLASMA is a clear, slightly alkaline, yellow fluid. It is less viscous than whole blood and consists of the following substances:

1. **Water**—90–93%.
2. **Blood proteins**—serum albumin, serum globulin and fibrinogen—7–9%.
3. **Salts**—0·9% made up largely of sodium chloride but with some calcium, magnesium, potassium, iron, phosphate, sulphate and bicarbonate ions also.
4. **Food substances**—amino-acids, glucose, fats and fatty acids—0·2–0·4%.

5. **Waste materials**—chiefly urea, uric acid and creatinine—0·0: 0·04%.
6. **Gases**—oxygen—to the limit of its solubility; nitrogen—to the lim of its solubility; carbon dioxide—only small amounts in simp solution because of the buffering action of sodium bicarbonat sodium phosphate, 'the blood proteins and the red corpuscles.
7. **Enzymes**.
8. **Hormones**—secretions from the endocrine glands.
9. **Antibodies**—substances which act against germs.
10. **Antitoxins**—substances which act against toxins or poisons.

Red corpuscle—*surface view*

Red corpuscle—*semilateral view*

envelope —stroma

Red corpuscle—*sectioned*

RED CORPUSCLES or ERYTHROCYTES are biconcave discs without nuclei, i.e. they are enucleate. There a about 5,000,000 red cells per cubic millimetre of blood. Singly they appear pale orange but in masses the give the blood its red colour.

Each corpuscle is 7μm in diameter and has an **envelope** surrounding a spongy mass called the **stroma**. T stroma contains the red pigment, **haemoglobin**, which is a complex protein containing iron and has the pow of combining reversibly with oxygen:

$$\text{haemoglobin} + \text{oxygen} \rightleftharpoons \text{oxy-haemoglobin}$$

In this way the red corpuscles carry a great deal of oxygen from the lungs to the other parts of the body.

The red corpuscles are short-lived. They originate in the red bone marrow of short, flat and irregula bones and the proximal ends of long bones. Production is stimulated by erythropoietin (see page 107 and vitamin C while maturation with accumulation of haemoglobin and loss of the originally large nucle requires the anti-anaemic factor of the liver, vitamin B_{12}. The mature, enucleate cells live in the blood stream for 100 to 120 days performing the function of oxygen transport. They then die and are broke down chiefly in the spleen. The iron from the haemoglobin is stored in the liver till required for makin new corpuscles while the residue forms the bile pigments and is removed from the body (see page 84)

WHITE CORPUSCLES or LEUCOCYTES are variable in size and shape but most of them are larger than the red corpuscles and each has a nucleus. There are normally 5 000–10 000 of them per cubic millimetre of blood but they increase in numbers during infection of the body by disease-producing organisms.

The main types of leucocyte with average percentages of each are as follows:

(A) **granulocytes** or **polymorphonuclear leucocytes** (65–75%)
(B) **non-granulocytes** or **mononuclear leucocytes** (25–35%).

A. **Polymorphonuclear leucocytes** are so called because their nuclei are large and lobulated. Their cytoplasm is granular and they are formed in bone marrow. Each granulocyte takes 10–14 days to mature and survives in circulation for about 10 hours before being destroyed in the lungs, intestines, liver, or spleen if it has not already passed into the peripheral tissues from which it cannot return. Granulocytes play a major role in inflammation in response to injury. They are capable of **amoeboid movement** and are attracted to any site of invasion by germs or other foreign particles. The process by which they ingest foreign particles and damaged tissue components is called **phagocytosis**. The alternative name for these cells refers to the granules, which stain characteristically:

(a) **neutrophils** (60–70%): granules stain with both acid and basic dyes—they are the most active of the phagocytes;
(b) **eosinophils** (2–4%): granules stain with acid dyes only—they increase in number during allergic reactions;
(c) **basophils** (0·5–2%): granules stain with basic dyes only—they manufacture **heparin** and **histamine**. Heparin is an anticoagulant (see page 91) while histamine causes small blood vessels to dilate.

B. **Mononuclear leucocytes** are so called because each cell has a single large round or slightly indented nucleus. They are formed in the lymph nodes and spleen and are divided into two main types:

(a) **monocytes** (2–8%): have few fine granules and are phagocytic, helping to defend the body by engulfing germs;
(b) **lymphocytes** (20–30%): have clear cytoplasm and a variety of functions. In general the larger lymphocytes appear to have **immunological competence**, i.e. induce immunity during disease and thus promote recovery, while the smaller are possibly memory cells responsible for retention of **induced immunity** over a number of years. Lymphocytes have a slow rate of production and considerable recirculation from the lymph nodes through the lymphatics to the blood and back. Foreign substances to which the lymphocytes respond are collectively called **antigens**. Response is, however, highly specific. Only a few of the larger lymphocytes become active on any one invasion. On stimulation by the antigen they change to **plasma cells** with conspicuous endo-plasmic network and a life span of only a few days. These cells produce **antibodies** which may be classified according to their type of action as: (i) **lysins** which dissolve invading organisms, (ii) **opsonins** which promote phagocytosis, (iii) **agglutinins** which cause bacteria and other cells to stick together in clumps, (iv) **precipitins** which act against soluble antigens causing precipitation.

Granulocyte

Monocyte

Large lymphocyt

Small lymphocyt

The action of antibodies cannot be completed without **complement**, a series of nine proteins produced by the liver. Once the antibody is attached to the antigen its shape changes and the components of complement become successively attached in the same way. Only after attachment of C^9 does destruction take place.

BLOOD PLATELETS are minute round discs which disintegrate rapidly when blood is shed to liberate substances that help clotting. There are about 300 000 of them per cubic millimetre of blood.

CLOTTING of blood is due to the following chain of events:
1. Injured tissue liberates a substance which can be converted by others in the plasma into the enzyme **thrombokinase** (thromboplastin). When blood **platelets** come into contact with a roughened or wettable surface, they break down and cause the formation of the same substance, but more slowly.
2. **Prothrombin** in the plasma is acted on by **thrombokinase** in the presence of calcium ions and becomes **thrombin**.
3. Thrombin acts on the blood protein, **fibrinogen**, converting it into **fibrin** which is tough and fibrous and which entangles the corpuscles to form the **clot**. The fluid which is squeezed out when the clot shrinks is called **serum**. Shrinkage due to contraction of fibrin.

Clotting of blood while in normal circulation is prevented by **antiprothrombin** or **heparin** which is formed by the liver and certain other tissues, including the lining of the blood vessels.

BLOOD GROUPS. The serum may contain agglutinins α and/or β which cause agglutination (clumping) of red corpuscles carrying the agglutinogens A and/or B respectively. It is dangerous for a patient to receive by transfusion any blood the corpuscles of which would be agglutinated by his serum, but his own corpuscles are not affected by any incoming serum. Blood grouping and other blood factors, e.g. the rhesus factor (Rh), are genetically controlled.

Blood group	AB	A	B	O
Agglutinogen present	A and B	A	B	O
Agglutinin present	None	β	α	α and β
Can receive blood types	AB, A, B and O	A and O	B and O	O only

The Functions of Blood
The functions of blood as a whole are the combined functions of its parts.
a) **Transport** —1. food from the alimentary canal to the tissues,
2. oxygen from the lungs to the tissues,
3. waste materials from the tissues to the excretory surfaces, e.g. carbon dioxide to the lungs, nitrogenous wastes to the kidneys,
4. hormones from the endocrine glands to other organs or tissues whose metabolism they control,
5. white corpuscles to the seat of infection,
6. heat from more active tissues to less active ones and to the skin for removal (see page 73).
b) **Protection**—1. salts provide a suitable environment for the life of the cells by maintaining a constant osmotic pressure and by their buffering action,
2. white corpuscles combat invading organisms,
3. clotting stops bleeding from wounds and helps to keep out germs,
4. white corpuscles help the healing of the wounds.

THE CIRCULATION

The blood can carry out its functions only when it is kept circulating in the blood-vessels. Thus the maintenance of the heart-beat and the unimpeded flow in the blood-vessels is essential to the life of the tissues. When the heart stops the whole body dies, while if the circulation to a part only is stopped, as in frostbite or too prolonged pressure with a tourniquet, that part alone may die. The most urgent and continuous need of the tissues is for oxygen, therefore the blood passes to the lungs and to the other organs alternately, the heart being completely divided to keep the oxygenated and the deoxygenated blood separate. The blood is carried from the heart in arteries, through the tissues in capillaries and back to the heart in veins. Many of the smaller arteries and veins form linked loops known as **anastomoses** which are safeguards against blockage.

1. The pulmonary circulation
A single **pulmonary artery** from the heart divides into two vessels, one to each lung, where further branching takes place to supply the lobes and lobules (see page 88). The finer arteries or **arterioles** supply the capillary network around the lung alveoli (see page 89). Venules collect the blood from the capillaries and join to form larger and larger veins which eventually leave the lungs as the four **pulmonary veins** which open directly into the heart.

2. The systemic circulation
a) **Arteries**. The **aorta** is the largest artery of the body. From it are given off the arteries to the various parts. These branch into arterioles which supply the capillary networks in the tissues.

PULMONARY CIRCULATION
capillaries of lungs
arterioles
venules
arteries
veins
HEART
arteries
veins
capillaries of most of body
arterioles
venules
sinusoids of liver
portal vein
capillaries of stomach, intestines, pancreas and spleen
SYSTEMIC CIRCULATION

Diagram of the course of the circulation

(b) **Veins.** Blood from the capillaries is collected into venules and then into veins. The veins are of two kinds, deep and superficial. The deep vei͏ are usually found following the corresponding arteries as **venae commitantes**, while the superficial veins drain the superficial venous networks a͏ open into the larger deep veins. The blood from the stomach, intestines, pancreas and spleen does not return to the heart directly. It is collect͏ into the **portal vein** and taken to the liver where it passes through vessels called sinusoids (see page 84). Blood from the liver passes into the inferi͏ vena cava.

The blood eventually reaches the heart through the two **venae cavae** and the **coronary sinus**. The superior vena cava drains the upper part of the bod͏ the inferior vena cava, the lower part of the body, and the coronary sinus, the heart tissue (see page 99).

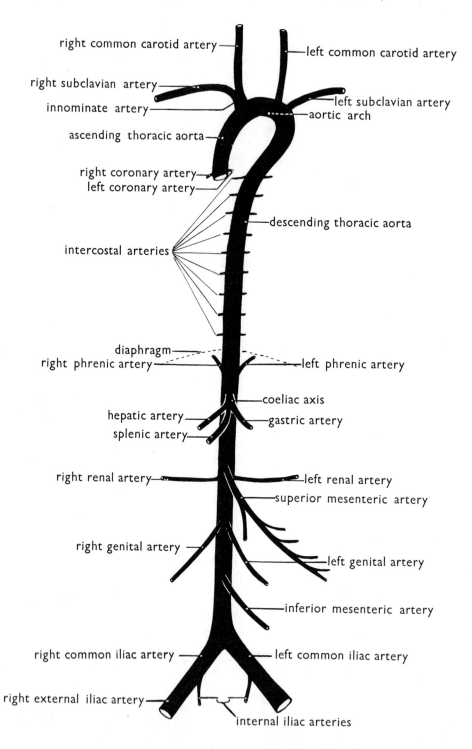

right common carotid artery

left common carotid artery

right subclavian artery

left subclavian artery

innominate artery

aortic arch

ascending thoracic aorta

right coronary artery
left coronary artery

descending thoracic aorta

intercostal arteries

diaphragm
right phrenic artery

left phrenic artery

coeliac axis

hepatic artery

gastric artery

splenic artery

right renal artery

left renal artery

superior mesenteric artery

right genital artery

left genital artery

inferior mesenteric artery

right common iliac artery

left common iliac artery

right external iliac artery

internal iliac arteries

Aorta and its branches

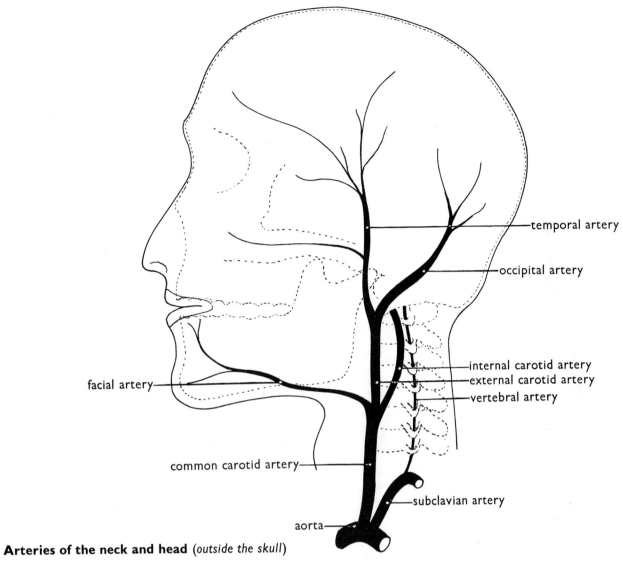

- temporal artery
- occipital artery
- internal carotid artery
- external carotid artery
- vertebral artery
- subclavian artery
- facial artery
- common carotid artery
- aorta

Arteries of the neck and head (*outside the skull*)

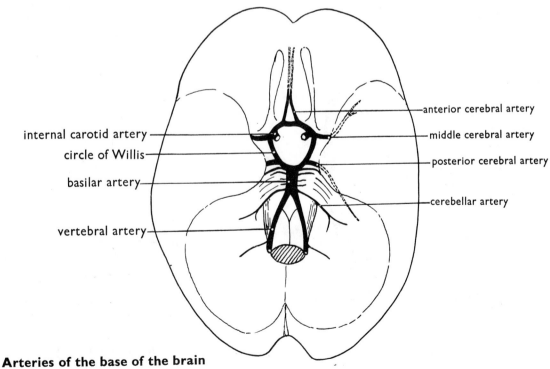

- internal carotid artery
- circle of Willis
- basilar artery
- vertebral artery
- anterior cerebral artery
- middle cerebral artery
- posterior cerebral artery
- cerebellar artery

Arteries of the base of the brain

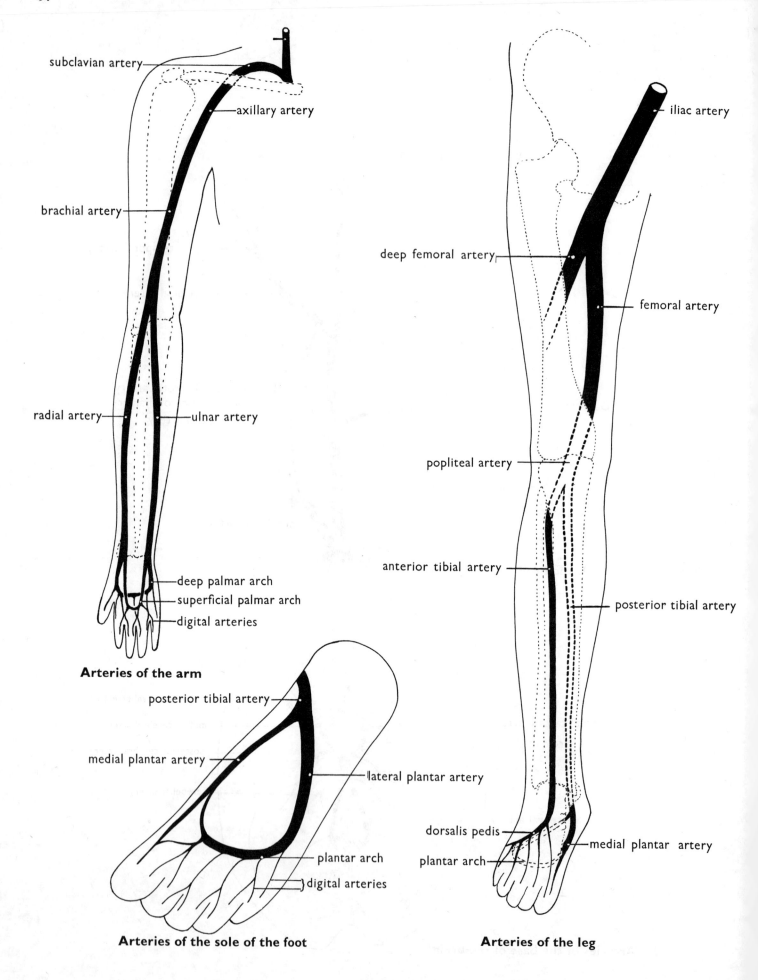

subclavian artery

axillary artery

brachial artery

radial artery — ulnar artery

deep palmar arch
superficial palmar arch
digital arteries

Arteries of the arm

iliac artery

deep femoral artery

femoral artery

popliteal artery

anterior tibial artery

posterior tibial artery

dorsalis pedis
plantar arch

medial plantar artery

Arteries of the leg

posterior tibial artery

medial plantar artery

lateral plantar artery

plantar arch
digital arteries

Arteries of the sole of the foot

The blood from the stomach, intestines, spleen and pancreas does not pass directly into the posterior vena cava but is collected in the **portal vein** and taken to the liver, where it passes through spaces in the liver tissue called **sinusoids** (see page 84) and mixes with the blood from the hepatic artery before reaching the hepatic veins.

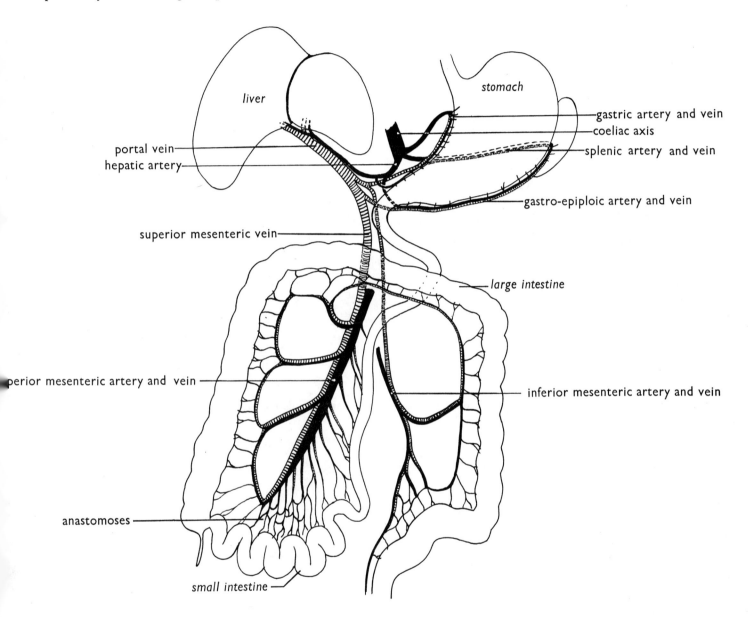

liver

stomach

gastric artery and vein

coeliac axis

portal vein

hepatic artery

splenic artery and vein

gastro-epiploic artery and vein

superior mesenteric vein

large intestine

perior mesenteric artery and vein

inferior mesenteric artery and vein

anastomoses

small intestine

Arteries and veins of the alimentary canal

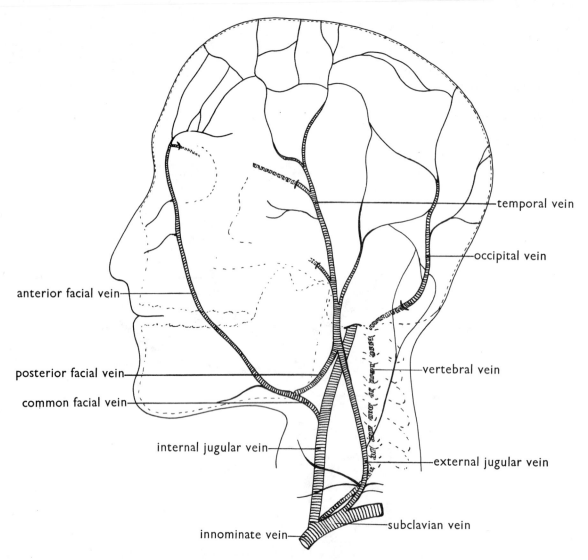

-temporal vein

-occipital vein

anterior facial vein-

posterior facial vein-

common facial vein-

-vertebral vein

internal jugular vein-

-external jugular vein

-subclavian vein

innominate vein-

Veins of the neck and head (*outside the skull*)

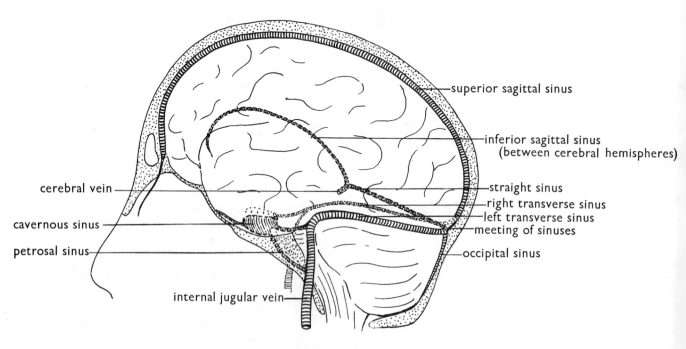

-superior sagittal sinus

-inferior sagittal sinus
(between cerebral hemispheres)

cerebral vein-

-straight sinus
-right transverse sinus
-left transverse sinus

cavernous sinus-

-meeting of sinuses

petrosal sinus-

-occipital sinus

internal jugular vein-

Venous sinuses (*inside the skull*)

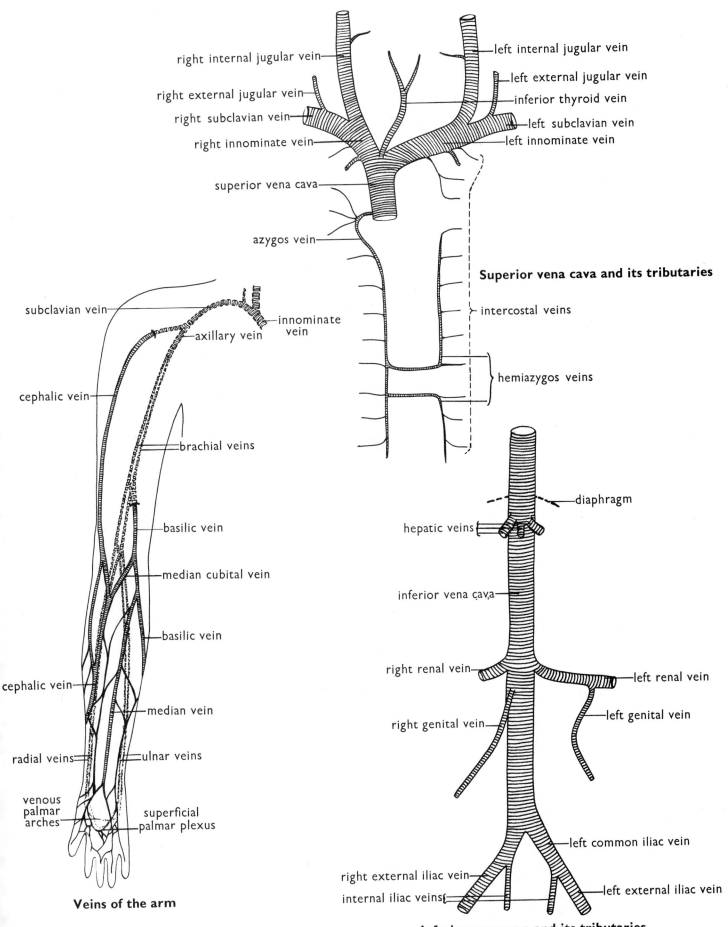

right internal jugular vein

left internal jugular vein

right external jugular vein

left external jugular vein

inferior thyroid vein

right subclavian vein

left subclavian vein

right innominate vein

left innominate vein

superior vena cava

azygos vein

Superior vena cava and its tributaries

intercostal veins

hemiazygos veins

subclavian vein

innominate vein

axillary vein

cephalic vein

brachial veins

diaphragm

hepatic veins

basilic vein

median cubital vein

inferior vena cava

basilic vein

cephalic vein

right renal vein

left renal vein

median vein

radial veins

ulnar veins

right genital vein

left genital vein

venous palmar arches

superficial palmar plexus

left common iliac vein

right external iliac vein

left external iliac vein

internal iliac veins

Veins of the arm

Inferior vena cava and its tributaries

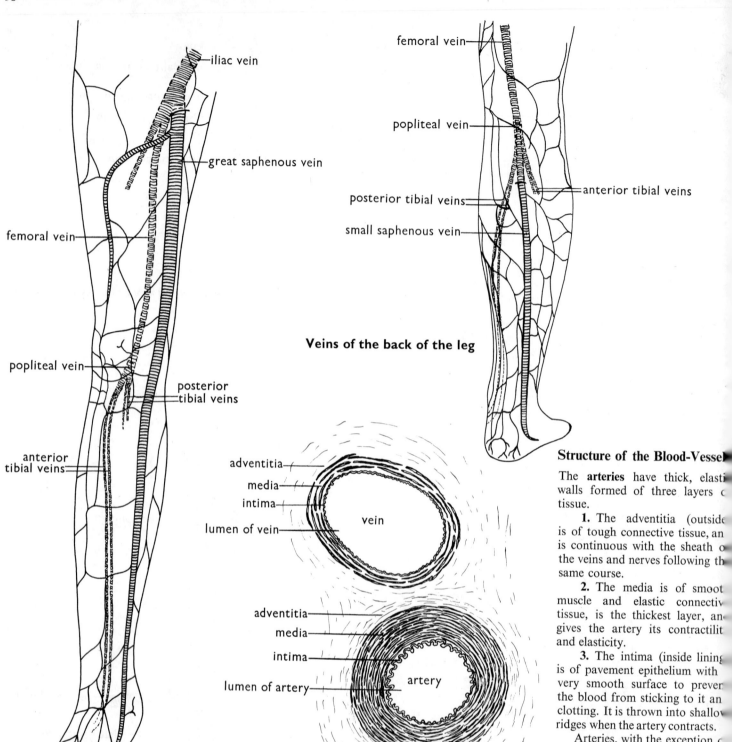

Veins of the back of the leg

iliac vein

great saphenous vein

femoral vein

popliteal vein

posterior tibial veins

anterior tibial veins

dorsal venous arch

Veins of the front of the leg

femoral vein

popliteal vein

posterior tibial veins

anterior tibial veins

small saphenous vein

adventitia

media

intima

lumen of vein

vein

adventitia

media

intima

lumen of artery

artery

T.S. Artery and Vein

Structure of the Blood-Vessels

The **arteries** have thick, elastic walls formed of three layers of tissue.

1. The adventitia (outside) is of tough connective tissue, and is continuous with the sheath of the veins and nerves following the same course.

2. The media is of smooth muscle and elastic connective tissue, is the thickest layer, and gives the artery its contractility and elasticity.

3. The intima (inside lining) is of pavement epithelium with a very smooth surface to prevent the blood from sticking to it and clotting. It is thrown into shallow ridges when the artery contracts.

Arteries, with the exception of the pulmonary artery, carry oxygenated blood which is under pressure from the elastic walls and flows in spurts as the heart beats.

The **veins** have thinner and less elastic walls than the arteries. They have the same three tissue layers but comparatively little media. Internally they possess pocket-shaped valves in pairs at irregular intervals. Veins, with the exception of the pulmonary veins, carry deoxygenated blood. The pressure of this blood is very low and smooth flow is maintained by:

(a) flow of blood from the capillaries,
(b) pressure from the surrounding organs, especially the skeletal muscles,
(c) the pairs of valves which prevent the backflow of blood,
(d) suction as the thorax expands during inhalation of breath.

Capillaries are exceedingly fine vessels which form networks in the tissues. Their walls are only one cell thick so that dissolved substances can diffuse through them to and from the tissues. The pressure in the capillaries is low, but higher than in the veins.

THE HEART

he heart is a hollow, muscular organ about the size of a closed fist. It lies in the thorax, between the lungs and above the diaphragm.

The heart is formed chiefly of muscle, the **myocardium**, but has an inner epithelial lining, the **endocardium**, and an outer covering of connective ssue and epithelium, the **pericardium**. The pericardium is a double-layered bag enclosing a cavity filled with pericardial fluid, which reduces iction as the heart moves during its beating.

The heart-muscle is supplied by the coronary blood-vessels.

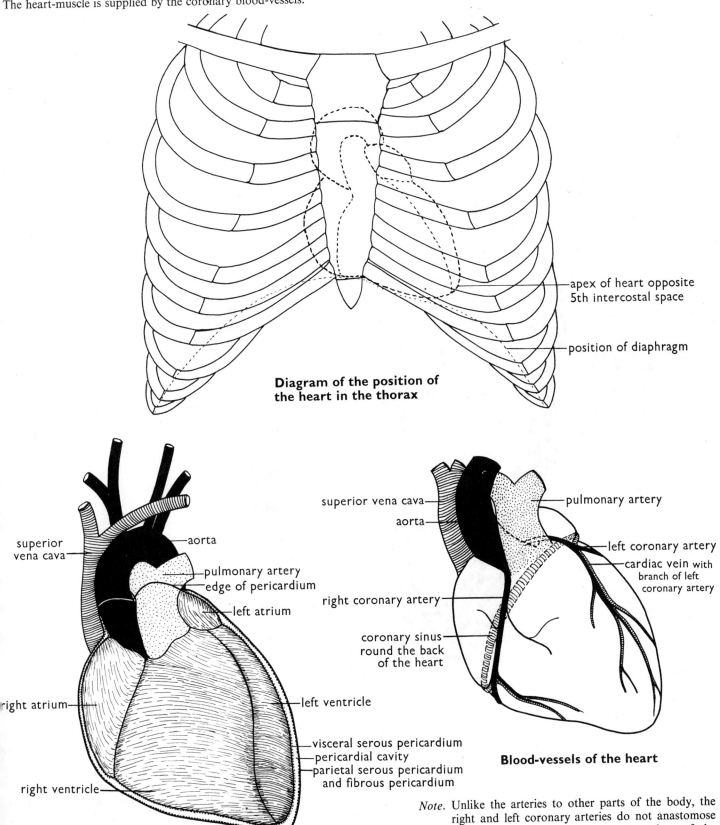

apex of heart opposite 5th intercostal space

position of diaphragm

Diagram of the position of the heart in the thorax

superior vena cava

aorta

pulmonary artery
edge of pericardium

left atrium

right atrium

left ventricle

visceral serous pericardium
pericardial cavity
parietal serous pericardium and fibrous pericardium

right ventricle

Heart, pericardium and great blood-vessels

superior vena cava
aorta

pulmonary artery

left coronary artery
cardiac vein with branch of left coronary artery

right coronary artery

coronary sinus round the back of the heart

Blood-vessels of the heart

Note. Unlike the arteries to other parts of the body, the right and left coronary arteries do not anastomose freely and therefore serve separate regions of the heart.

THE HEART, continued

The cavity of the heart is divided completely by a median partition called the septum and each side is further divided into a thin-walled atrium above and a thick-walled ventricle below. Each atrium communicates with the corresponding ventricle by an atrio-ventricular aperture. Thus there are four chambers in the heart to each of which blood-vessels are connected. In situ in the thorax, the right atrium and ventricle lie in front of the left atrium and ventricle.

The right atrium receives deoxygenated blood from the **superior vena cava**, the **inferior vena cava** and the **coronary sinus**.

The right ventricle sends deoxygenated blood into the **pulmonary artery**.

The left atrium receives oxygenated blood from the four **pulmonary veins**.

The left ventricle sends oxygenated blood into the **aorta**.

THE VALVES

The direction of flow of blood is maintained by valves. Between the right atrium and the right ventricle is the **tricuspid valve** with three parts, each of which is supported at its free edges by tendinous strands, the **chordae tendineae**, the other ends of which are attached to the papillary muscles.

Between the left atrium and the left ventricle is the **bicuspid** or **mitral valve** which is similar to the tricuspid valve but has only two parts.

At the mouth of the pulmonary artery and at that of the aorta there are three pocket-shaped, **semi-lunar valves**, while the openings of the inferior vena cava and coronary sinus each have a single pocket-shaped valve.

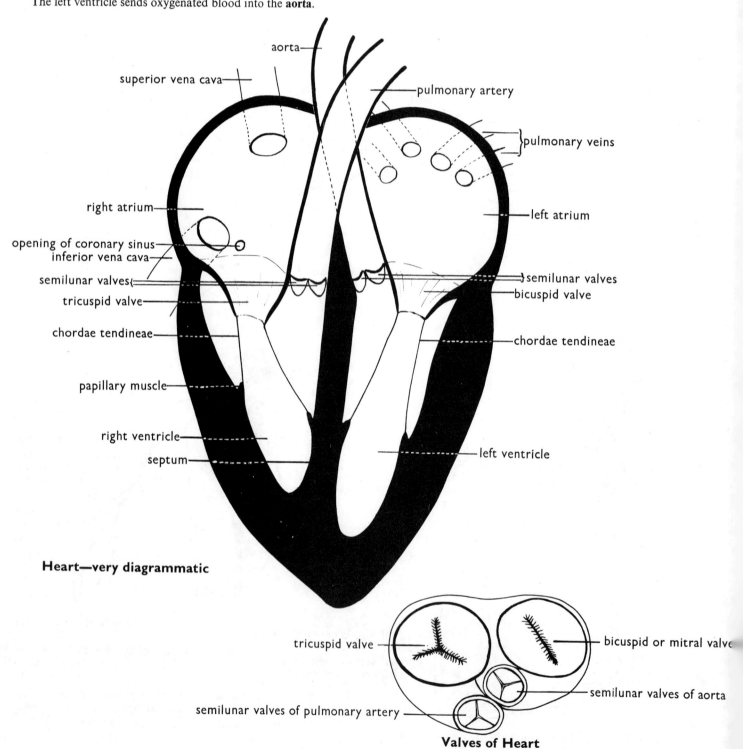

Heart—very diagrammatic

Valves of Heart

HEART-BEAT

The heart - muscle contracts rhythmically with a period of relaxation and rest between each contraction. The contraction period is called systole, the dilation period, diastole, and the whole repetitive process is the cardiac cycle.

Atrial systole. The atria contract and force blood into the ventricles so that they are distended and filled with blood under pressure. The contraction affects the regions round the mouths of the veins first so that these vessels are closed and blood cannot flow back into them.

Ventricular systole. The ventricles contract and force blood, under pressure, past the semilunar valves into the arteries. Back-flow of blood into the atria is prevented by the tricuspid and bicuspid valves respectively. The papillary muscles keep the chordae tendineae taut so that the valves are held in place. At the same time the muscles of the atria relax and blood begins to flow into them from the veins.

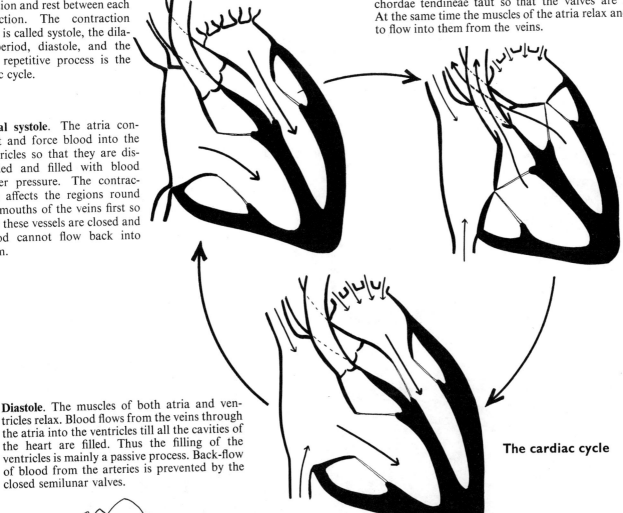

Diastole. The muscles of both atria and ventricles relax. Blood flows from the veins through the atria into the ventricles till all the cavities of the heart are filled. Thus the filling of the ventricles is mainly a passive process. Back-flow of blood from the arteries is prevented by the closed semilunar valves.

The cardiac cycle

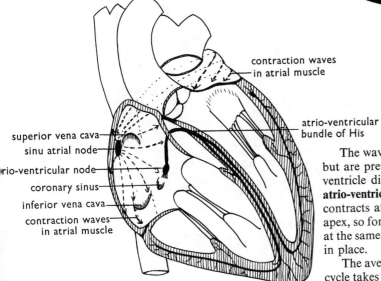

superior vena cava
sinu atrial node
atrio-ventricular node
coronary sinus
inferior vena cava
contraction waves in atrial muscle

contraction waves in atrial muscle

atrio-ventricular bundle of His

Diagram to show the transmission of the contraction wave through the heart-muscle

The rate of the heart-beat is controlled by the **sinu-atrial node**, composed of special cardiac muscle which contracts rhythmically without nervous stimulation, but which is affected by the **sympathetic** and **parasympathetic nerves**. The sympathetic fibres from the **cardiac plexus** accelerate while the parasympathetic fibres from the **vagus** slow the rate of the rhythmic impulse formation at the node (see page 62).

The waves of contraction pass from fibre to fibre through the atrial muscles but are prevented by a connective tissue ring from reaching the muscle of the ventricle directly. The impulses are transmitted to the ventricle through the **atrio-ventricular node** and the **atrio-ventricular bundle of His.** Thus the ventricle contracts after the atrial contraction is complete. Its contraction starts at the apex, so forcing blood up into the arteries. Contraction of the papillary muscles at the same time increases the tension on the chordae tendinae to keep the valves in place.

The average rate of heart-beat is 72 per minute. Thus each complete cardiac cycle takes 0·8 sec. This is divided between systole and diastole as follows:

Atrial systole 0·1 sec.	Atrial diastole 0·7 sec.
Ventricular systole 0·3 sec.	Ventricular diastole 0·5 sec.
Therefore complete systole 0·4 sec.	Complete diastole 0·4 sec.

BLOOD-PRESSURE

Blood-pressure in the arteries is greater during systole than during diastole. Measured in the brachial artery, an average healthy adult has a systolic pressure of 120 mm mercury, a diastolic pressure of c. 70 mm mercury and therefore a pulse pressure (the difference) of c. 50 mm mercury. Excess weight, smoking and stress all contribute to raised blood pressure and heart strain.

THE LYMPHATIC SYSTEM

The **lymphatic system** is really a part of the vascular system.

Blood is contained in a closed system of vessels—the arteries, veins and capillaries—and is kept circulating by the heart, but some of the fluid part, the plasma, escapes from the capillaries by diffusion and filtration and bathes the tissues directly. This **tissue fluid** becomes **lymph** when it is collected up in the lymph vessels, through which it is returned to the blood-stream. Thus the composition of lymph is similar to that of blood plasma, but it has less protein, less food materials and more waste materials. It contains white but no red corpuscles, and the lymphocytes are relatively more numerous.

The **lymph vessels** start as fine, blind-ended, lymph capillaries. These join to form lymphatics which are similar to veins in general course and structure, but are more numerous and fine and have many more semilunar valves.

lymphatics

veins

lymph glands

lymph capillaries

heart

blood capillaries

arteries

The relationship of the lymph system to the blood system

direction of flow of lymph

position of valve

portion of ves—
cut open

valve

Lymphatic vessel

afferent lymph vessel

afferent lymph vessel

lymph path

cortex

medulla

trabecula

lymphoid tissue

recticulum

artery

vein

efferent lymph vessel

Lymph gland

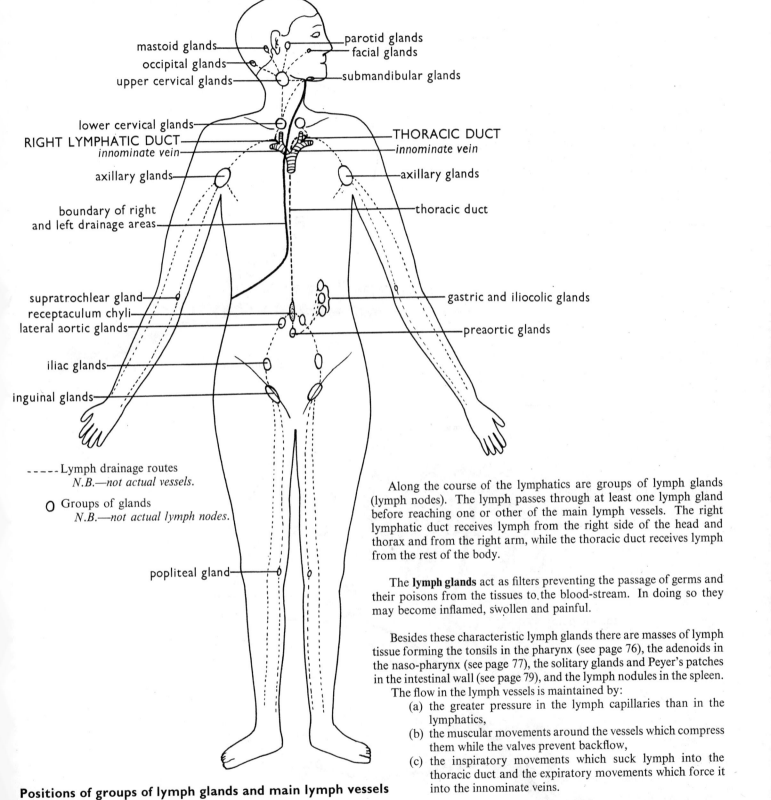

mastoid glands
occipital glands
upper cervical glands

parotid glands
facial glands
submandibular glands

lower cervical glands
RIGHT LYMPHATIC DUCT
innominate vein

THORACIC DUCT
innominate vein

axillary glands

axillary glands

boundary of right
and left drainage areas

thoracic duct

supratrochlear gland
receptaculum chyli
lateral aortic glands

gastric and iliocolic glands

preaortic glands

iliac glands

inguinal glands

- - - - - Lymph drainage routes
   N.B.—not actual vessels.

O Groups of glands
   N.B.—not actual lymph nodes.

popliteal gland

Positions of groups of lymph glands and main lymph vessels

Along the course of the lymphatics are groups of lymph glands (lymph nodes). The lymph passes through at least one lymph gland before reaching one or other of the main lymph vessels. The right lymphatic duct receives lymph from the right side of the head and thorax and from the right arm, while the thoracic duct receives lymph from the rest of the body.

The **lymph glands** act as filters preventing the passage of germs and their poisons from the tissues to the blood-stream. In doing so they may become inflamed, swollen and painful.

Besides these characteristic lymph glands there are masses of lymph tissue forming the tonsils in the pharynx (see page 76), the adenoids in the naso-pharynx (see page 77), the solitary glands and Peyer's patches in the intestinal wall (see page 79), and the lymph nodules in the spleen.
   The flow in the lymph vessels is maintained by:
   (a) the greater pressure in the lymph capillaries than in the lymphatics,
   (b) the muscular movements around the vessels which compress them while the valves prevent backflow,
   (c) the inspiratory movements which suck lymph into the thoracic duct and the expiratory movements which force it into the innominate veins.

THE SPLEEN

The spleen lies below the diaphragm, behind and to the left of the stomach. Its shape and size vary with movements of the adjacent organs and with the degree of distention of the organ itself.

The Structure of the Spleen

The structure of the spleen is similar to that of a lymph node (see page 102), with fibrous trabeculae supporting a pulpy mass of reticulate cells and phagocytic spleen cells, but instead of lymph the spaces between these cells contain blood which comes, therefore, into direct contact with the splenic cells (cf. the sinusoids of the liver—see page 84).

Scattered in the splenic pulp are lymph nodules each containing an arterial network and surrounded by a marginal zone containing short, straight, penicillate arterioles on each of which is a swelling called an ellipsoid. The arterioles open into the venous sinusoids from which blood is eventually removed through pulp veins.

The Functions of the Spleen

The spleen controls the quality and volume of the blood in circulation.

1. It destroys worn out red blood-corpuscles.
2. It acts as a reservoir for blood-cells of all kinds.
3. It produces lymphocytes in the lymph nodules.
4. It produces red corpuscles and granulocytes during foetal life and on certain occasions in adult life, e.g. after severe haemorrhage.

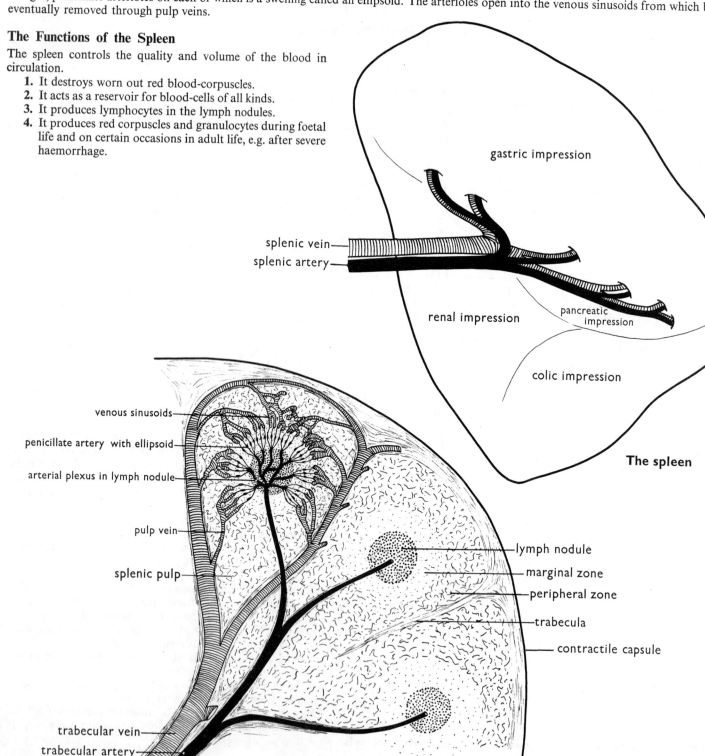

The spleen

Diagram to show the structure of the spleen

THE EXCRETORY SYSTEM

EXCRETION

The chief waste products which have to be removed from the body are: **1.** indigestible and undigested residues of food, **2.** carbon dioxide from oxidation processes, **3.** nitrogenous waste from the breakdown of proteins, **4.** excess salts, **5.** water, **6.** heat. They are excreted through the alimentary canal, lungs, skin and kidneys.

(a) The **alimentary canal** removes the residues of the food through the anus by defaecation. These residues take with them negligible heat and water, some salts and special waste materials such as the bile pigments.

(b) The **lungs** remove the carbon dioxide. Considerable quantities of water and heat may be lost incidentally if the inspired air is dry or cold.

(c) The **skin** removes excess heat not lost through breathing. Loss of heat is aided by evaporation of sweat. The sweating, incidentally, removes some nitrogenous waste, salts and water.

(d) The **kidneys** remove the nitrogenous waste and excess salts not removed by sweating and the excess water not lost through sweating or breathing.

Because the kidneys balance the system and remove the metabolic waste materials not lost in other ways, they, with their ducts, are called the excretory system.

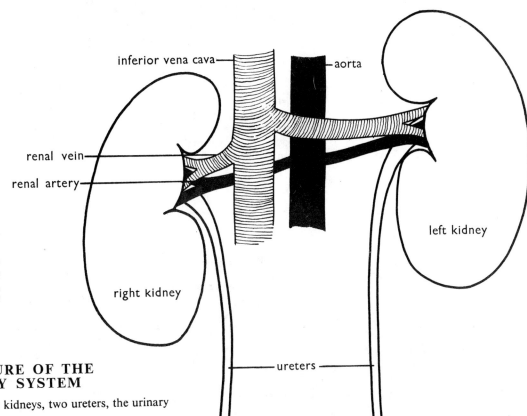

THE STRUCTURE OF THE EXCRETORY SYSTEM

The excretory system consists of two kidneys, two ureters, the urinary bladder and the urethra.

The **kidneys** lie against the back wall of the abdomen behind the liver and stomach, covered by peritoneum and embedded in fat.

The **bladder** lies in the front of the pelvis and the **ureters** curve round the lower part of the abdomen to meet it.

The **urethra** of the female is short (4 cm) and opens in front of the vagina. The urethra of the male is joined by the reproductive ducts and is elongated to open on the tip of the penis (approximately 20 cm). (See pages 113 and 111.)

THE STRUCTURE OF THE KIDNEY

Each kidney is a bean-shaped organ about 11 cm long, 5 cm broad and 3 cm thick. It has a fibrous capsule covering the outside and lining the renal sinus. The kidney substance is arranged to form about fourteen lobes, each of which has granular cortex surrounding the base and part of the sides of a pyramid of striated medulla. The apex or papilla of each pyramid lies in a cup-shaped cavity called a calyx. The calyces join to form the wide pelvis of the ureter.

The kidney tissue is made up of numerous **renal tubules** which produce the urine. The glomerular capsules and convoluted parts of the tubules lie in the convoluted substance of the cortex while the loops of Henle and collecting ducts lie in the medullary rays and in the medulla. Close to each glomerulus are groups of cells forming the **juxtaglomerular apparatus**, which has endocrine function (see page 107).

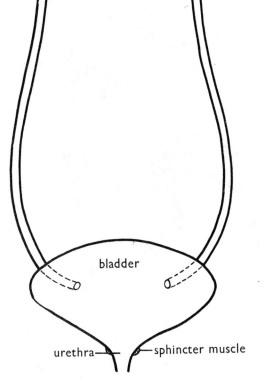

Excretory system

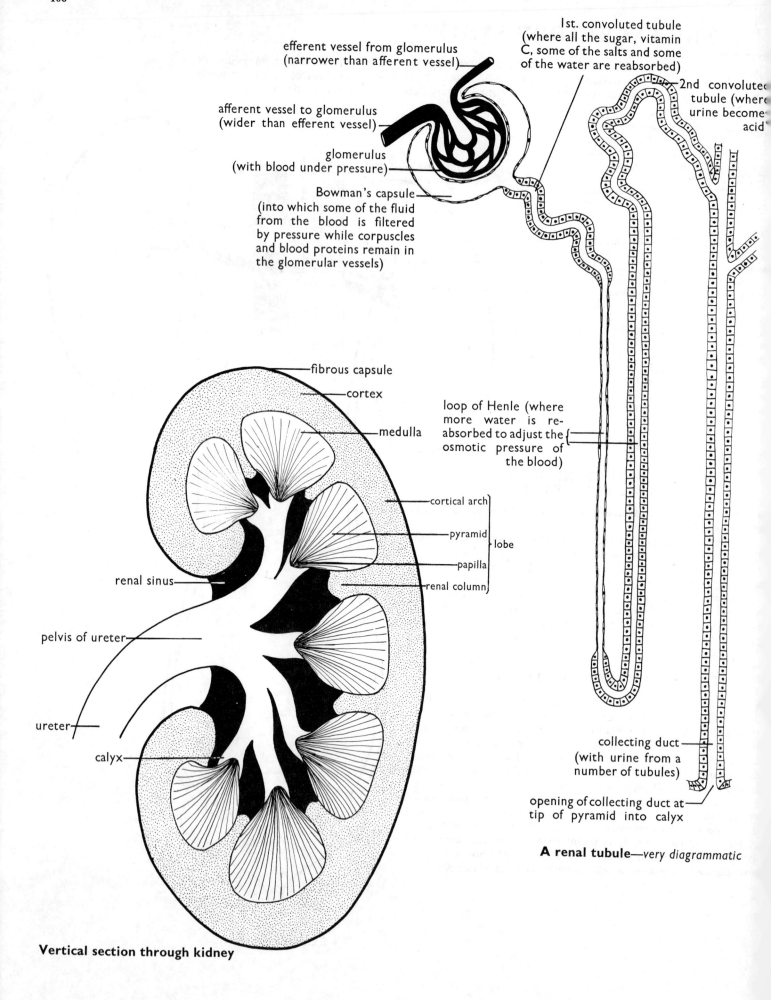

efferent vessel from glomerulus
(narrower than afferent vessel)

afferent vessel to glomerulus
(wider than efferent vessel)

glomerulus
(with blood under pressure)

Bowman's capsule
(into which some of the fluid
from the blood is filtered
by pressure while corpuscles
and blood proteins remain in
the glomerular vessels)

1st. convoluted tubule
(where all the sugar, vitamin
C, some of the salts and some
of the water are reabsorbed)

2nd convoluted
tubule (where
urine becomes
acid)

fibrous capsule

cortex

medulla

cortical arch ⎤
pyramid ⎬ lobe
papilla ⎪
renal column ⎦

loop of Henle (where
more water is re-
absorbed to adjust the
osmotic pressure of
the blood)

renal sinus

pelvis of ureter

ureter

calyx

collecting duct
(with urine from a
number of tubules)

opening of collecting duct at
tip of pyramid into calyx

A renal tubule—*very diagrammatic*

Vertical section through kidney

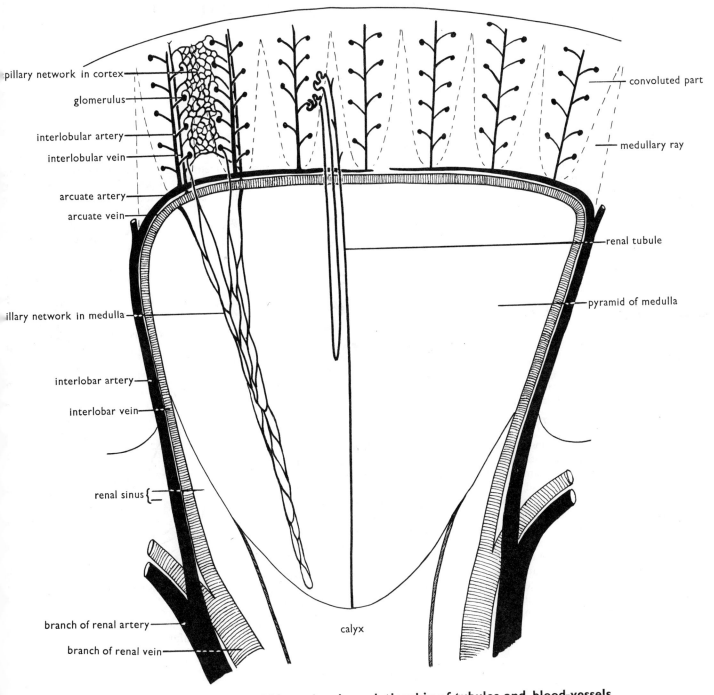

pillary network in cortex

glomerulus

interlobular artery

interlobular vein

arcuate artery

arcuate vein

illary network in medulla

interlobar artery

interlobar vein

renal sinus {

branch of renal artery

branch of renal vein

convoluted part

medullary ray

renal tubule

pyramid of medulla

calyx

Diagram of a lobe of the kidney showing relationship of tubules and blood-vessels

he Functions of the Kidneys

. EXCRETORY. The kidneys produce **urine**, the average composition of hich is 96% water, 2% salts, and 2% nitrogenous waste chiefly in the rm of **urea**. Variations in the composition of urine reflect the ability f the kidneys to regulate water and salt content of the body fluids. Vater retention is promoted by a secretion from the pituitary body hile sodium retention and potassium loss are promoted by one of the ormones of the adrenal cortex (see page 109). Losses of water and alts in other ways are balanced. When there is little perspiration, as in old weather, the urine tends to be copious and dilute, while in hot veather it is less in quantity and more concentrated. The quantity and oncentration are also affected by the amount drunk. The sensation of iirst is itself a reaction to minute increase in osmotic pressure of the lood affecting special cells in the hypothalamus region of the brain. he average quantity of urine formed in 24 hours is 1 litre.

2. SECRETORY. The cells of the juxtaglomerular apparatus produce two hormones, **renin** and **erythropoietin**. Renin is concerned with maintenance of blood pressure. If blood pressure in the renal artery falls, renin is released and converts one of the blood proteins to **angiotensin,** which constricts arterioles thus increasing blood pressure. As a result of this increase in blood pressure, the production of renin falls so the system is self-regulatory. Erythropoietin controls production of erythrocytes by red bone marrow (see page 90).

The Bladder

The bladder is very extensible and very elastic. It can hold up to about a pint (350–400 ml) of urine, but it is usually emptied when the contents reach about 150 ml. The passing of urine is called **micturition** and is under voluntary control because the sphincter muscle at the neck of the bladder is supplied by voluntary nerves. At the same time the smooth muscle of the bladder wall and pressure from the abdominal muscles help to expel the urine.

THE ENDOCRINE SYSTEM

The glands found in the body are of two kinds: **1. exocrine glands** which secrete into cavities or ducts: **2. endocrine glands** which secrete into blood-stream.

EXOCRINE GLANDS may be unicellular, e.g. goblet cells; or multicellular. The latter are:

   (i) simple tubular, e.g. gastric glands
   (ii) branched tubular, e.g. gastric glands and crypts of Lieberkuhn
   (iii) coiled tubular, e.g. salivary glands
   (iv) simple alveolar, e.g. sebaceous glands
   (v) compound or racemose, e.g. salivary glands, liver, pancreas and mammary glands.

The exocrine glands frequently produce mucus and/or enzymes (e.g. the digestive glands). Sometimes they secrete non-enzymatic materi with special functions (e.g. sebaceous and mammary glands). Sometimes they excrete waste materials as well as other substances (e.g. sweat glan and liver). None of the materials produced by the exocrine glands can have any effect on other living cells or tissues in the body, except those the ducts and passages into which the secretions are passed.

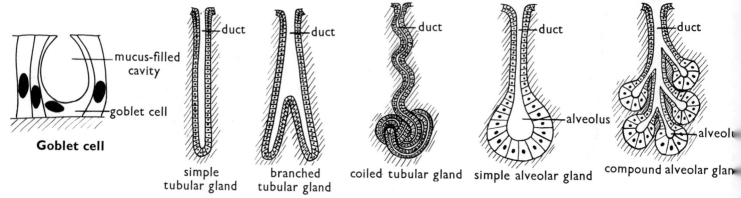

Types of multicellular glands

ENDOCRINE GLANDS are usually groups of special cells either within other organs or as separate organs. Often they are like racemose glands without ducts. The **hormones** which they produce pass into the blood stream and are the chemical messengers which control many of the functions of other cells and tissues.

The chief endocrine glands are the **pituitary body**, and the **supra-renal, thyroid,** and **parathyroid glands**, but many organs have subsidiary endocrine functions, e.g. the **thymus** (page 110), the **pancreas** (page 82), the **stomach** (page 78), the small **intestines** (page 79), the **kidneys** (page 107), the **testes** (page 111), the **ovaries** (page 113), and the **placenta** (page 115). The endocrine function of the **pineal body** is uncertain.

The **hypothalamus** is not listed as an endocrine organ though it has ultimate control over much of the system through the pituitary body, with which it is considered.

In health, the entire endocrine system is self-regulatory, therefore malfunctioning of one part may bring about malfunctioning of others.

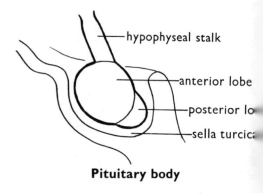

Pituitary body

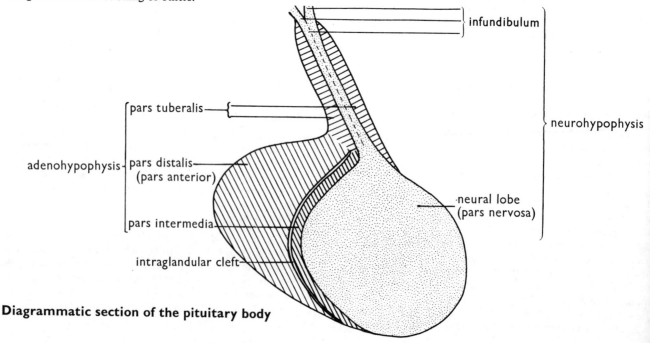

Diagrammatic section of the pituitary body

The pituitary body lies in the sella turcica of the sphenoid bone, underneath and attached to the brain (see page 56). The **infundibulum** or neural stalk and the **pars nervosa** or neural lobe develop from the brain of the embryo and constitute the **neurohypophysis**. The infundibulum is also part of the hypothalamus, thus there is close connection between the autonomic centres of the latter and the neurohypophysis. The **pars anterior, pars intermedia,** and **pars tuberalis** develop from non-nervous tissue and constitute the **adenohypophysis**, which is served by portal veins from the hypothalamus.

Note. The terms posterior lobe and anterior lobe represent morphological division through the intraglandular cleft and do not correspond to division in origin and function.

The Functions of the Pituitary Body

THE NEUROHYPOPHYSIS. Two hormones, **oxytocin** (pitocin) and **pitressin** (vasopressin), have been extracted from the neurohypophysis, but it is now thought they are manufactured in the hypothalamus and passed to the neurohypophysis for storage till stimulation of the hypothalamic nerve centres triggers their release.

Oxytocin stimulates the contraction of the **smooth muscle** of the uterus and the breasts. It is produced during childbirth, and during lactation, when it helps ejection of milk (see page 117).

Pitressin, in spite of its name, is primarily an **antidiuretic**, increasing the permeability of the distal convoluted and collecting tubules of the kidneys so that more water is returned to the blood stream and the urine becomes more concentrated. Deficiency of pitressin causes diabetes insipidus. The vasopressor effect, raising blood pressure by contraction of arterioles, is negligible in man.

THE ADENOHYPOPHYSIS. Though the adenohypophysis is often called the 'master gland of the endocrine system' it is itself under the control of hormonal substances called releasing factors secreted by the hypothalamus and carried to it in the portal blood supply. The adenohypophysis produces at least 7 hormones.

1. The **adrenocorticotropic hormone (ACTH)** controls the activity of the adrenal cortex, particularly the production of glucocorticoids and sex hormones.

2. The **thyrotropic hormone (TSH)** controls the activity of the thyroid gland. Intense emotion and cold increase the production by the hypothalamus of the releasing factor and thus of TSH. The consequent increase in thyroxine (see page 110) enhances the effects of adrenalin.

3. The **growth hormone (GH)** favours protein synthesis by promoting nitrogen retention. Its most obvious effects are increase in skeletal development. Excess of the growth hormone during childhood causes gigantism, and in adults, acromegaly. Deficiency causes dwarfism.

4. The **melanocyte stimulating hormone (MSH)** brings about darkening of the skin, but is normally inhibited by the hormones of the adrenal cortex.

5. and 6. The two **gonadotropic hormones,** the **follicle stimulating hormone (FSH)** and the **luteinising hormone (LH)** are so called because of their effects on the follicles of the ovaries and the corpora lutea respectively (see page 113). In men, FSH stimulates seminiferous tissue and LH the interstitial tissue (see page 111).

7. The **luteotropic** or **lactogenic hormone (LTH)** stimulates the production of milk by the mammary glands and helps to maintain the corpora lutea during the lactation period. The oestrogens from the ovaries inhibit LTH production. During lactation, active LTH production temporarily inhibits production of FSH and thus of oestrogens. (Some authorities believe LTH to be identical with GH.)

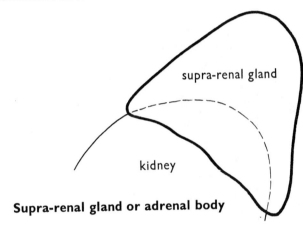

Supra-renal gland or adrenal body

THE SUPRA-RENAL GLANDS OR ADRENAL BODIES

One of these glands lies capping each kidney. Each gland has an outer layer or **cortex** derived from the same tissue as the kidneys and the reproductive organs, and an inner region or **medulla** derived from the same tissue as the sympathetic cords.

The Functions of the Supra-renal Glands

1. THE ADRENAL CORTEX. Over 50 adrenal cortical hormones are now known, all of which are chemically classified as **steroids**. They are divided as follows.

(a) **Mineralocorticoids** control mineral salt content of extra-cellular fluids, particularly the levels of sodium, potassium, and chloride, by affecting the permeability of the renal tubules to these ions. Excess tends to lead to retention of body fluid and thus oedema.

(b) **Glucocorticoids** affect metabolism by increasing breakdown of protein, deposition of liver glycogen, the amount of blood glucose, total body fat, and erythrocyte production, but decreasing the number of circulating lymphocytes and thus antibody formation and having an anti-inflammatory effect. They also depress pituitary secretion of ACTH, TSH, and MSH (see above). Glucocorticoid activity increases in response to stress.

(c) **Sex hormones** including androgens which mimic the effects of the testicular hormones (page 111) and oestrogens and progesterones which mimic the effects of the ovarian hormones (page 113).

2. THE ADRENAL MEDULLA. The secretion of the adrenal medulla known as **adrenaline** contains two closely related substances, **epinephrine** and **norepine-**

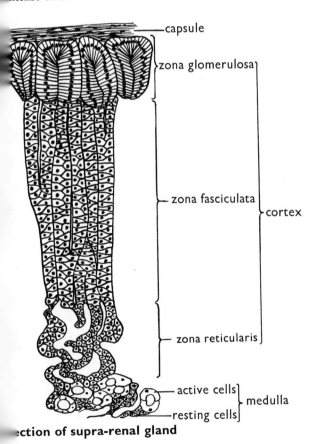

capsule
zona glomerulosa
zona fasciculata — cortex
zona reticularis
active cells — medulla
resting cells

Section of supra-renal gland

phrine. The effects of these two substances mimic those produced by stimulation of the sympathetic nervous system (see page 62). Epinephrine is most active in increasing breakdown of glycogen in the liver and also cardiac output and ACTH and TSH production, while norepinephrine brings about generalised vasoconstriction. Norepinephrine is known to be produced in the sympathetic ganglia as well as in the adrenal medulla.

THE THYROID GLAND

The main parts of this gland lie on either side of the larynx and the trachea and are joined by the isthmus below the larynx.

The thyroid gland consists of many closed vesicles containing gelatinous colloidal material into which thyroxine is secreted. It is richly supplied with blood-vessels through which the hormone is eventually removed.

The Functions of the Thyroid Gland

The thyroid gland produces a group of **iodine**-containing hormones the best known of which, **thyroxine,** controls the general **metabolic rate,** increasing many specific metabolic processes, rate of heart beat, blood pressure, mental activity, fertility and growth, but decreasing the secretion of the thyrotropic hormone by the adenohypophysis and thus regulating its own production. Swelling of the gland, called **goitre,** may be due to deficiency of iodine or over-activity of the secretory vesicles. Under-activity of the gland causes **cretinism** in children and **myxoedema** in adults.

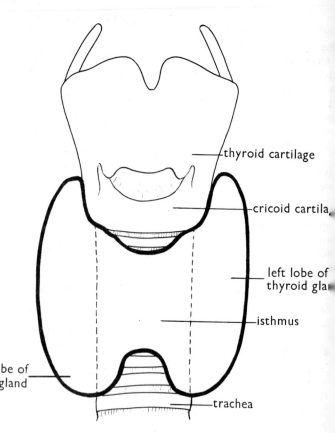

Thyroid gland

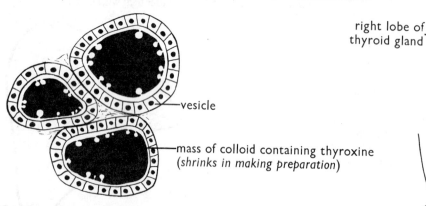

Section of a group of thyroid vesicles (high power)

THE PARATHYROID GLANDS

There are usually four of these glands behind the thyroid gland.

The Functions of the Parathyroid Glands

The secretion of these glands is called **parathormone.** It helps to maintain a constant level of **calcium** in the blood by promoting mobilisation from bone when there is dietary deficiency. At the same time it stimulates the kidneys to clear the blood of the extra **phosphate** so liberated.

THE THYMUS

The thymus lies behind the sternum, over the roots of the great blood vessels. It is large in infants but does not increase in size as rapidly as the body and, from puberty onwards, gradually degenerates, most of its characteristic lymphoidal cells being replaced by adipose tissue.

The Functions of the Thymus

Before birth the thymus is the major source of **lymphocytes** and of the precursor cells from which **lymph nodes** and **spleen** develop. The thymus continues to produce lymphocytes throughout life, especially when there has been depletion through stress. Thus it is important in creating and maintaining **immunity** (see page 90). Two hormones have been isolated from thymus tissue: **thymosin** which stimulates growth of lymphoid tissue, and **promine** which stimulates general growth. Both hormones are most important in early life when growth is fastest and immunities are being established.

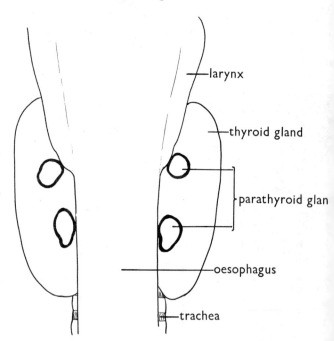

Parathyroid glands

THE PINEAL BODY

The pineal body lies on the roof of the brain above the corpo quadrigemina (see page 56). It degenerates and completely calcif in many adults, but, while of glandular structure, the hormo **melatonin** can be extracted from it. Melatonin has no kno function in man though it reduces skin pigmentation in frogs a may thus be considered as a physiological vestige in the same w as the pineal body is itself a vestige of a third eye.

THE REPRODUCTIVE SYSTEM

e differences between men and women are basically genetic. Men normally have one X chromosome and one Y chromosome, while women have
) X chromosomes. The primary effect of the appropriate sex chromosomes is to cause the reproductive organs to develop as **testes** or **ovaries**,
ich produce the reproductive cells, **spermatozoa** and **eggs** respectively, and which also produce hormones responsible for secondary sexual charac-
s. The male reproductive system is designed to produce numerous very minute spermatozoa, to store them and to transfer them to the reproductive
sages of the female. The female reproductive system is designed to produce a smaller number of eggs and to provide the young with a suitable
ce to grow and with nourishment during the early part of its life.

THE MALE REPRODUCTIVE SYSTEM

e reproductive system of the male consists of two **testes**, two **vasa
ferentia**, two **ejaculatory ducts**, two **seminal vesicles, prostate** and
bo-urethral glands, and **penis**.

E TESTES. The testes develop in the abdomen, but just before birth
·y descend to the groin and come to lie outside the abdominal cavity
the bags of skin called the scrotal sacs. Each testis is an ovoid body
·med of many seminiferous tubules bound together by interstitial
sue. The walls of the tubules produce **spermatozoa** while the **inter-
tial tissue** produces the male hormones, collectively called **androgens**,
which **testosterone** is the most important. The androgens are respon-
·le for the development of sexual characteristics including growth of
·ard and deepening of voice.

E DUCTS AND GLANDS. Leading from each testis are numerous fine
·cts, the vasa efferentia, which join a mass of coiled tubules called the

epididymis in which the immature and non-motile spermatozoa become
mature and are stored till required. From the epididymis there is a
single duct, the vas deferens, which with the spermatic artery and the
spermatic vein forms the spermatic cord. This runs through the
inguinal canal to the abdominal cavity.

The vasa deferentia are joined by the seminal vesicles and together
form the ejaculatory ducts which open into the urethra. The prostate
and bulbo-urethral glands open into the urethra directly. These glands
and the seminal vesicles produce secretions which contribute to the
volume of the seminal fluid and increase the motility and viability of
the spermatozoa.

THE PENIS. The penis is short and soft when not in use, but contains
special strands of cavernous tissue which can be distended with blood
and thus stiffened. The urethra opens at the tip of the penis and
spermatozoa can be injected through it into the vagina of the female.

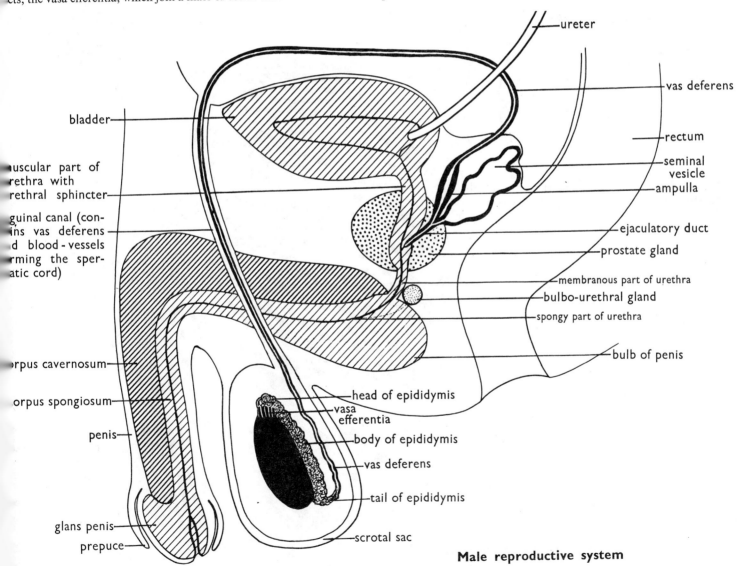

Male reproductive system

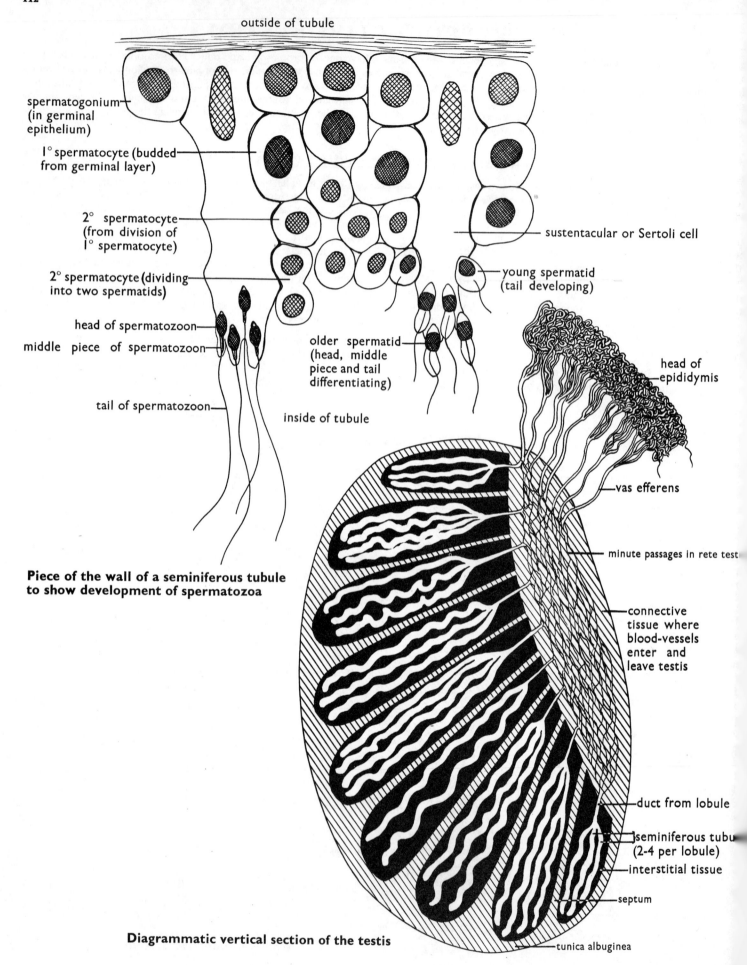

outside of tubule

spermatogonium
(in germinal
epithelium)

1° spermatocyte (budded
from germinal layer)

2° spermatocyte
(from division of
1° spermatocyte)

2° spermatocyte (dividing
into two spermatids)

head of spermatozoon

middle piece of spermatozoon

tail of spermatozoon

sustentacular or Sertoli cell

young spermatid
(tail developing)

older spermatid
(head, middle
piece and tail
differentiating)

inside of tubule

**Piece of the wall of a seminiferous tubule
to show development of spermatozoa**

head of
epididymis

vas efferens

minute passages in rete testi

connective
tissue where
blood-vessels
enter and
leave testis

duct from lobule

seminiferous tubu
(2-4 per lobule)

interstitial tissue

septum

tunica albuginea

Diagrammatic vertical section of the testis

THE FEMALE REPRODUCTIVE SYSTEM

he reproductive system of the female consists of two **ovaries** nd their ducts, the **uterine tubes**, **uterus**, and **vagina**. The agina opens into the **vestibule** behind the urethra and etween folds of tissue called the **labia**. In front of the urethra pening is a small, highly sensitive projection called the itoris which is a vestigeal penis.

HE **OVARIES**. The ovaries lie in the pelvic basin and are held position by the broad ligament and the ligament of the ary. The germinal epithelium surrounds a mass of connec- ve tissue called stroma in which the young **ova** develop. Each eveloping ovum is surrounded by a group of cells forming a llicle. Rupture of the ripe follicles to release immature ova called **ovulation**. After ovulation, the follicles fill with llow cells and become the **corpora lutea** which normally ow for 10–15 days and then atrophy, but one at least is tained throughout a pregnancy.

THE **VAGINA, UTERUS, AND UTERINE TUBES**. The **vagina** is the passage into which the penis is inserted during **copulation**. It leads into the thick-walled **uterus**, the neck of which is called the **cervix**. Attached to the uterus are two narrow **uterine** or **Fallopian tubes** up which spermatozoa must pass if **fertilisation** is to take place. Only a few hundred of the many million spermatozoa in a single ejaculation of seminal fluid reach the upper ends of the tubes into which the ova are drawn by the cilia on the numerous processes called **fimbriae** around its funnel-shaped opening. Of the ova shed at any ovulation, only one normally matures. A single spermatozoon may fertilise this and the embryo then develops as described on the following two pages. Unfertilised and immature ova pass through the uterus and vagina to the exterior and are wasted.

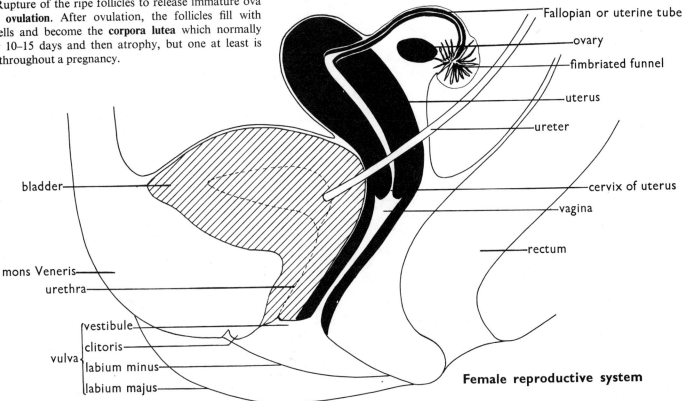

Female reproductive system

HE **MENSTRUAL CYCLE**. The ovaries produce at least six hormones called estrogens which are responsible for the development of female sexual charac- ristics. The corpora lutea produce **progesterone** which supplements the action f the oestrogens in thickening the uterine mucosa ready for possible implantation f an embryo and preparing the mammary glands for lactation. From puberty menopause, except during pregancy, ovulation takes place at monthly tervals, governed by the alternating increase of the two **gonadotropic hormones** ee page 109). FSH stimulates ripening of the follicles and secretion of oestro- ens. The oestrogens in turn suppress secretion of FSH and increase secretion of H which then promotes development of the corpora lutea. As the corpora lutea trophy, secretion of both progesterone and the oestrogens is reduced, secretion f FSH increases again, the uterine mucosa breaks down, and menstrual bleeding ccurs. During pregnancy large quantities of oestrogens and progesterone are roduced by the placenta (see page 115), ovulation is inhibited, corpora lutea and ickening of uterine mucosa are maintained, and there is no menstruation.

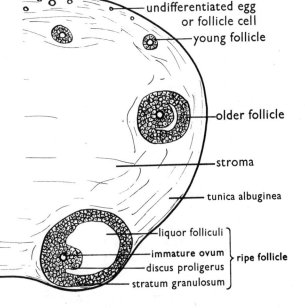

Diagrammatic section of ovary with follicles in various stages of development

EMBRYOLOGY

The prenatal development of the baby is termed embryology.

The fertilised egg is a single cell, but this very soon divides to from a sphere of cells. The sphere becomes hollow and is called the blastocyst. Its outer wall is the trophoblast and on one side is a mass of cells, the germinal disc, from which the embryo develops. The germinal disc is originally on the surface but becomes enclosed by growth of the amnion over it. The cells become differentiated into three tissue layers called ectoderm, endoderm and mesoderm. The ectoderm of the germinal disc forms the skin and its derivatives and the nervous tissue of the embryo. Ectoderm also forms the trophoblast and the lining of the amniotic cavity. Endoderm forms the lining of the yolk sac (a vestige of the sac which encloses the yolk in the eggs of birds and reptiles) and later forms the lining of the alimentary canal and its associated glands. Mesoderm lies between the ectoderm and the endoderm and gives rise to all connective tissues including blood and bones, to all muscle tissue and to reproductive tissue.

The blastocyst becomes implanted in the uterine mucosa and forms villi from the trophoblast to increase the surface of contact.

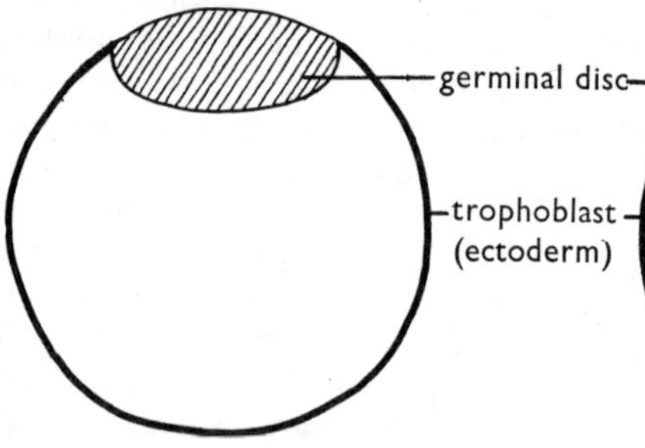

Young blastocyst

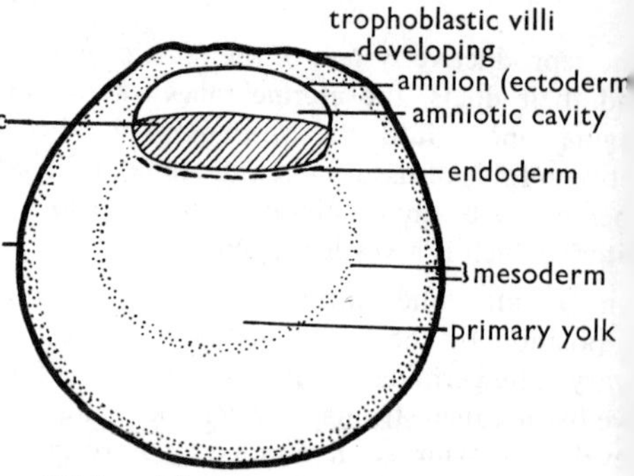

Older blastocyst about to become implanted

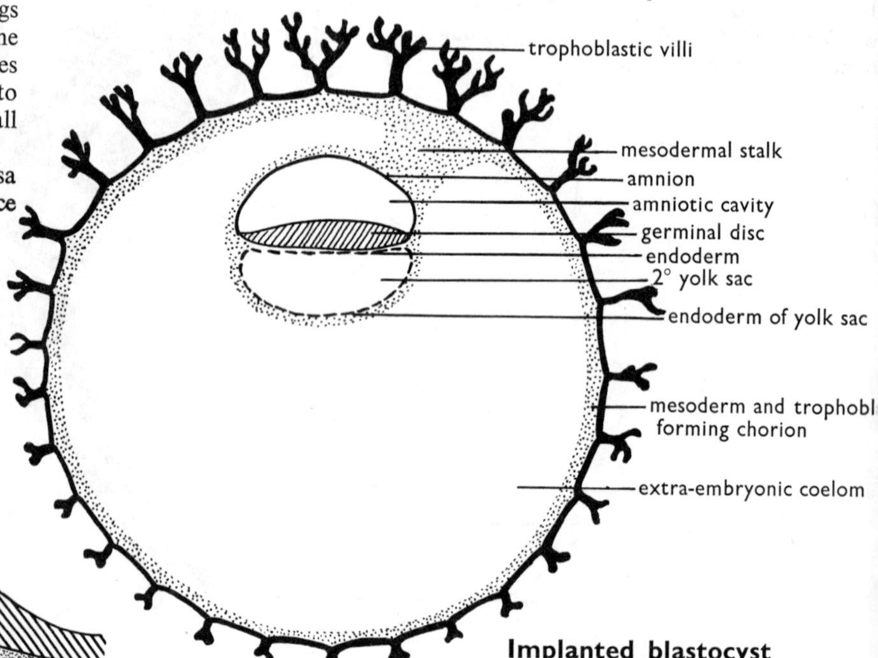

Implanted blastocyst

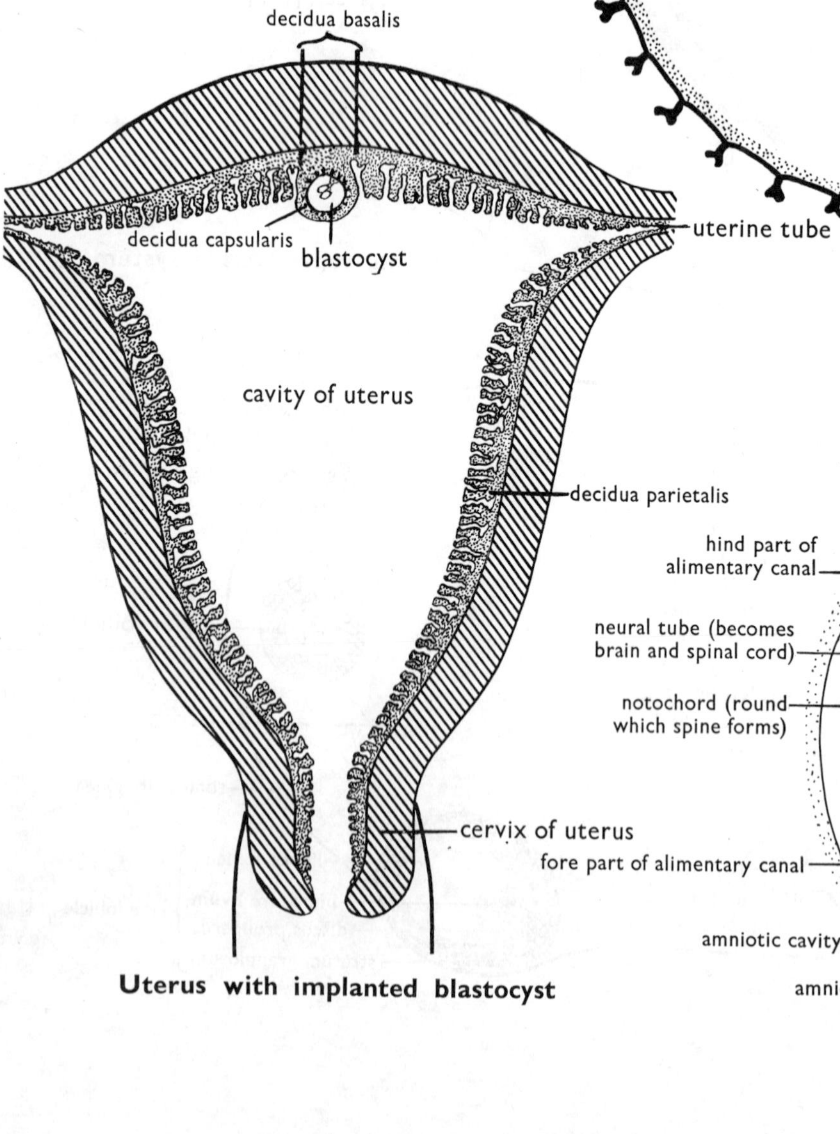

Uterus with implanted blastocyst

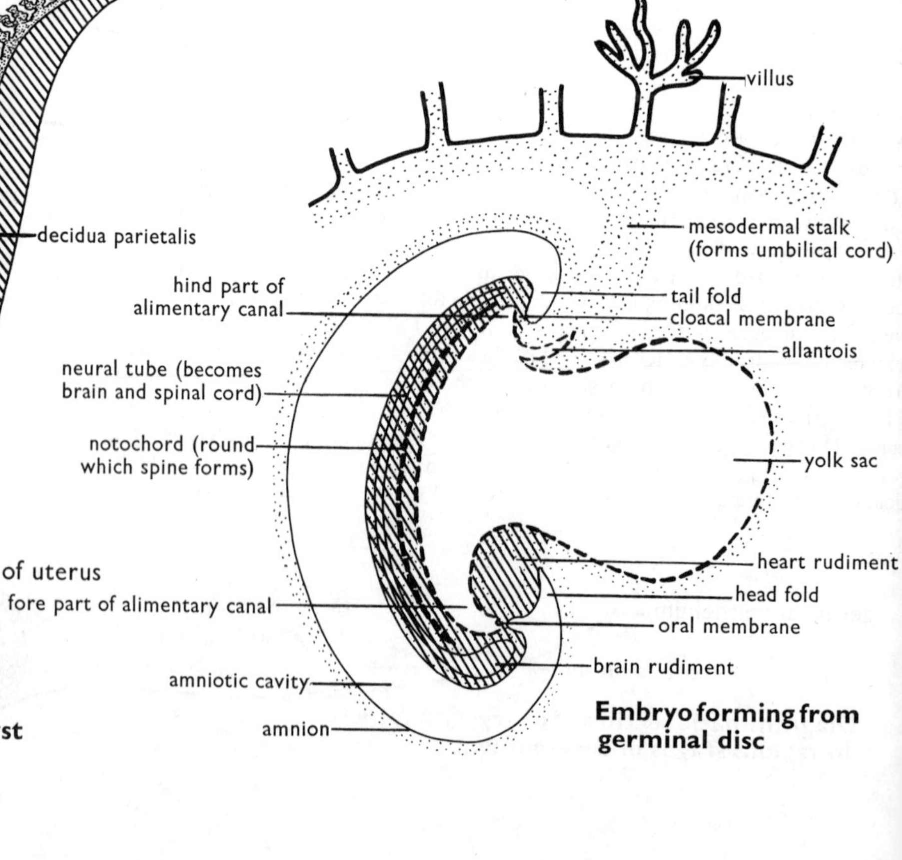

Embryo forming from germinal disc

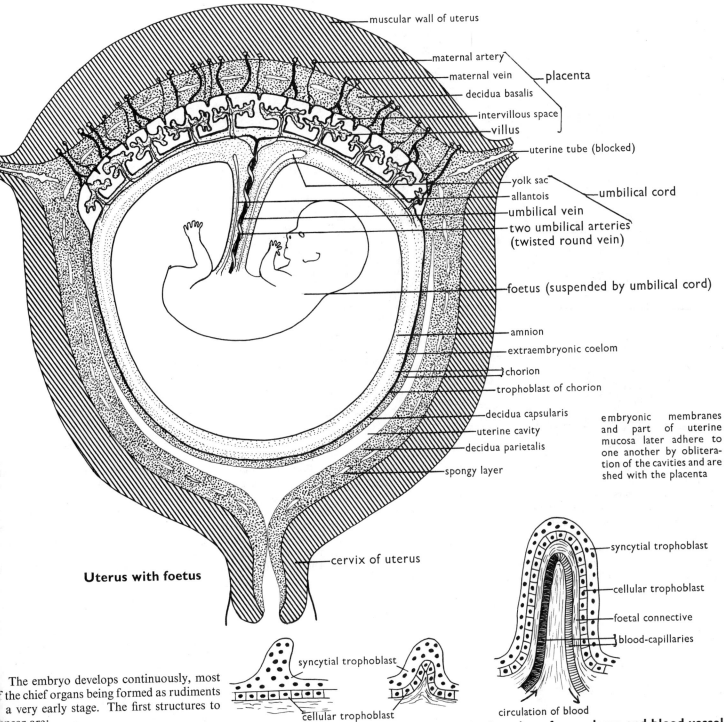

muscular wall of uterus

maternal artery
maternal vein — placenta
decidua basalis
intervillous space
villus

uterine tube (blocked)

yolk sac
allantois — umbilical cord
umbilical vein
two umbilical arteries
(twisted round vein)

foetus (suspended by umbilical cord)

amnion
extraembryonic coelom
chorion
trophoblast of chorion

decidua capsularis
uterine cavity
decidua parietalis

spongy layer

embryonic membranes and part of uterine mucosa later adhere to one another by obliteration of the cavities and are shed with the placenta

Uterus with foetus

cervix of uterus

syncytial trophoblast
cellular trophoblast
foetal connective
blood-capillaries

syncytial trophoblast

cellular trophoblast

circulation of blood

1° **villus**　　　　2° **villi forming by invasion of mesoderm and blood-vessels**

The embryo develops continuously, most of the chief organs being formed as rudiments at a very early stage. The first structures to appear are:

1. the neural tube which gives rise to the brain and spinal cord,

2. the notochord which forms a support and is later replaced by the vertebrae,

3. the mesodermal blocks which give rise to the chief muscles,

4. the head and tail folds which shut in the alimentary canal and form the under side of the embryo,

5. the heart and blood-vessels which form a functioning circulation at a very early stage.

Note. The outgrowth of the hind part of the alimentary canal called the allantois is a vestige of an important structure found in birds and reptiles.

The delicate developing embryo is suspended in, and protected by, fluid in the cavity enclosed by the amnion. The fluid in the extra-embryonic coelom between the amnion and the outer embryonic membrane or chorion has the same effect until the cavity is obliterated later in development by the union of amnion and chorion.

As the embryo grows bigger, it and its membranes project into the uterine cavity. The villi are invaded by connective tissue and later by blood vessels. The compound structure of the villi and the uterine mucosa forms the **placenta** through which the embryo, now called the foetus, is fed, receives oxygen and gets rid of waste materials. Blood sinuses form in the maternal portion of the placenta and surround the villi, but the maternal blood is always completely separated from the foetal blood by the cellular layer of the trophoblast. The trophoblast has a selective filtering action which prevents the entry of maternal hormones into the foetus (especially important when the foetus is male) and of many poisons, drugs and germs. In addition to **oestrogens** and **progesterone** (see page 113), the placenta secretes **chorionic gonadotropin**, which reinforces the lactogenic action of the luteotropic hormone (see page 117).

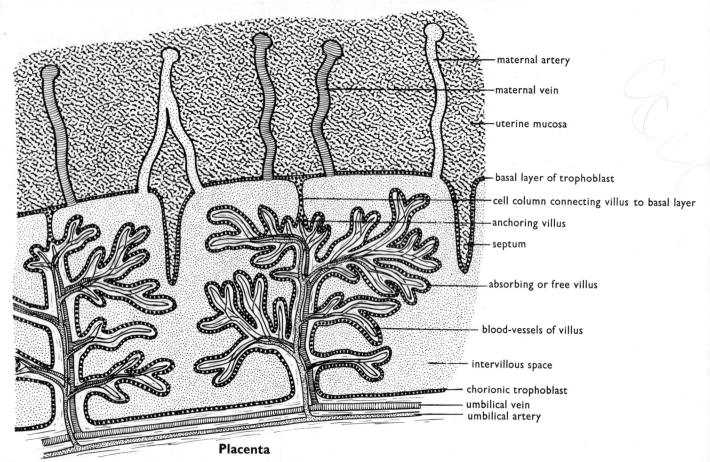

Placenta

The connection between the foetus and the placenta is by the **umbilical cord**, in which there are two arteries, one vein and the allantoic canal. The **umbilical arteries** are branches of the iliac arteries. The blood from the **umbilical vein** reaches the inferior vena cava chiefly through the **ductus venosus**, but some also travels indirectly through the liver.

Before birth the **foramen ovale** (in the septum between the atria of the heart) and the **ductus arteriosus** (between the left pulmonary artery and the aorta) allow short-circuiting of the blood so that very little goes to the, as yet, non-functioning lungs. The valve of the inferior vena cava directs the blood from this vessel through the foramen ovale without mixing with the blood from the superior vena cava.

At birth, or **parturition**, the foramen ovale and the ductus arteriosus close so that the normal double circulation is established (except in 'blue' babies). The umbilical cord is cut so that the baby is dependent on its own lungs for a supply of oxygen and on food taken through the mouth and must get rid of its own waste materials.

The placenta and the embryonic membranes are shed as the **afterbirth**.

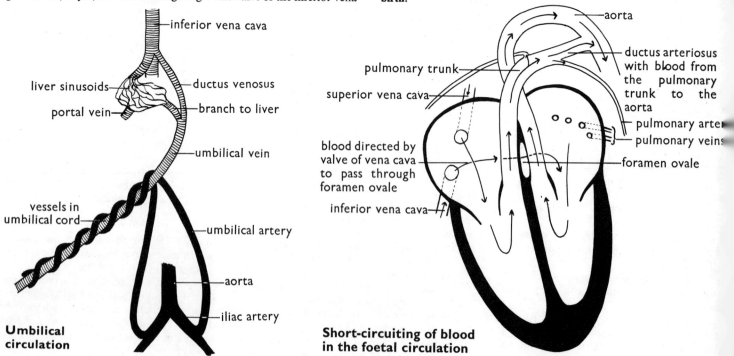

Umbilical circulation

Short-circuiting of blood in the foetal circulation

THE MAMMARY GLANDS

Mammary glands are present in both sexes, and lie outside the wall of the chest, over the 2nd to 6th ribs. Those of the female swell at puberty under the influence of the sex hormones.

Each breast has 12–20 **lobes**, subdivided into **lobules**, the walls of which bear very numerous glandular **alveoli**. Lobules and lobes are bound together by fatty connective tissue. The **lactiferous ducts** from the lobules open into wide **lactiferous sinuses** from each of which a short, straight duct leads to the nipple. Around the nipple, the corrugated area of skin called the **areola** becomes darkly pigmented after pregnancy.

The Function of the Mammary Glands

The mammary glands do not become functional till after childbirth. During pregnancy, the large quantities of oestrogens formed by the placenta inhibit formation of lactogenic hormones, but they and progesterone give rise to additional growth of the breasts and sensitise their secretory tissue. At parturition, oestrogen secretion ceases and secretion of the luteotropic hormone (LTH) and the glucocorticoids (see page 109) is increased. The **lactogenic** action of these hormones causes the alveoli to become active.

The initial secretion from the mammary glands is a yellowish fluid containing protein and sugar but no fat. This is called **colostrum** and is replaced by **milk** within 2–3 days. The average composition of milk is:

Protein 1·5–2·0% (⅓ is lactalbumen, ⅔ is caseinogen)
Fat 3·5%
Milk sugar (lactose) 6·5%
Mineral salts, including calcium, 0·3% (*Note.* Milk is deficient in iron but normally enough iron is stored in the liver of the foetus to last the baby till it begins to take a mixed diet.)
Vitamins A, B, C, and D
Water 87·7–88·2%

Milk is the perfect food for the young infant and its composition varies with the age of the baby, becoming gradually more concentrated as the child's digestion improves. Provided suckling continues, lactation will be fully maintained for 7–9 months, or during the time that the corpus luteum is still yielding progesterone, but if suckling is discontinued, capacity for milk production is soon lost.

The reaction to suckling is a complex chain of events, starting with stimulation of the nerve endings in the nipple. Nerve impulses reaching the brain affect the hypothalamus and produce two responses:

(a) decrease in formation of the prolactin inhibiting hormone so that the pituitary body releases additional LTH which stimulates milk production,

(b) release of oxytocin which affects the muscle in the walls of the alveoli, forcing milk through the ducts into the lactiferous sinuses from which it is easily available to the nursing baby.

At the height of lactation, up to 1·5 litres of milk may be formed each day. To supply the nutrients for this it is important for the mother to have adequate supplies in her own diet. It is particularly important for her to take supplementary calcium, phosphate, and vitamin D to guard against decalcification of her bones and teeth.

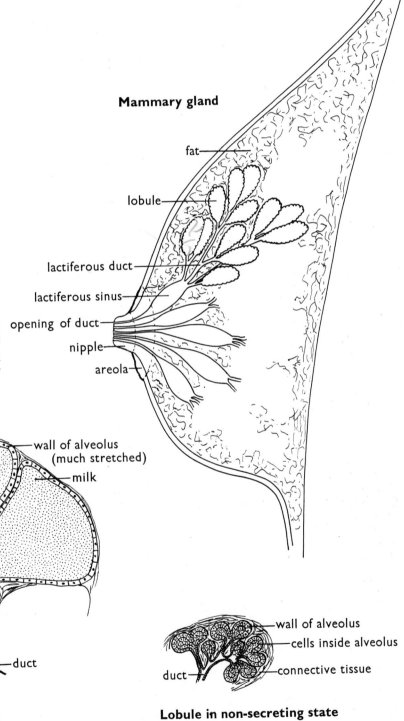

Lobule in secreting state

Lobule in non-secreting state

Index